www.EffortlessMath.com

... So Much More Online!

- ✓ FREE Math lessons
- ✓ More Math learning books!
- ✓ Mathematics Worksheets
- ✓ Online Math Tutors

Need a PDF version of this book?

Send email to: Info@EffortlessMath.com

STAAR Grade 6 Math Prep 2020

A Comprehensive Review and Step-By-Step Guide to Preparing for the STAAR Math Test

By

Reza Nazari & Ava Ross

Reza Nazari & Ava Ross

All inquiries should be addressed to:

info@effortlessMath.com

www.EffortlessMath.com

ISBN–13: 978-1-64612-186-1

ISBN–10: 1-64612-186-4

Published by: Effortless Math Education

www.EffortlessMath.com

Description

STAAR Grade 6 Math Prep 2020, which reflects the 2020 STAAR grade 6 test guidelines, provides students with the confidence and math skills they need to ace the STAAR Math test. This comprehensive Prep book with hundreds of examples, over 2,000 sample questions, and two full length STAAR Grade 6 Math tests is all you will ever need to fully prepare for the STAAR Math. It will help you hone your math skills, overcome your exam anxiety, and boost your confidence -- and do your best to succeed on the STAAR Math Test.

Whether you are intimidated by math, or even if you were the first to raise your hand in the Math classes, this book can help you incorporate the most effective method and the right strategies to prepare for the STAAR Grade 6 Math test successfully. ***STAAR Grade 6 Math Prep 2020*** is a breakthrough in Math learning — offering a winning formula and the most powerful methods for learning basic Math topics confidently.

The surest way to succeed on STAAR Math Test is with intensive practice in every math topic tested--and that's what you will get in ***STAAR Grade 6 Math Prep 2020***. Each chapter of this focused format has a comprehensive review created by Test Prep experts that goes into detail to cover all of the content likely to appear on the STAAR Grade 6 Math test. Not only does this all-inclusive workbook offer everything you will ever need to conquer STAAR Math test, it also contains two full-length and realistic STAAR Grade 6 Math tests that reflect the format and question types on the STAAR to help you check your exam-readiness and identify where you need more practice.

Inside the pages of this comprehensive prep book, students can learn math topics in a structured manner with a complete study program to help them understand essential math skills. It also has many exciting features, including:

- Content 100% aligned with the 2020 STAAR test
- Written by STAAR Math tutors and test experts
- Complete coverage of all STAAR Grade 6 Math concepts and topics which you will be tested
- Step-by-step guide for all STAAR Grade 6 Math topics
- Over 2,000 additional STAAR math practice questions in both multiple-choice and grid-in formats with answers grouped by topic, so you can focus on your weak areas
- Abundant Math skill building exercises to help test-takers approach different question types that might be unfamiliar to them
- 2 full-length practice tests (featuring new question types) with detailed answers

STAAR Grade 6 Math Prep 2020 is the only book you'll ever need to master Basic Math topics! It can be used as a self–study course – you do not need to work with a Math tutor. (It can also be used with a Math tutor)

Ideal for self-study as well as for classroom usage.

About the Author

Reza Nazari is the author of more than 100 Math learning books including:
– **Math and Critical Thinking Challenges:** For the Middle and High School Student
– **GRE Math in 30 Days**
– **ASVAB Math Workbook 2018 - 2019**
– **Effortless Math Education Workbooks**
– **and many more Mathematics books ...**

Reza is also an experienced Math instructor and a test–prep expert who has been tutoring students since 2008. Reza is the founder of Effortless Math Education, a tutoring company that has helped many students raise their standardized test scores—and attend the colleges of their dreams. Reza provides an individualized custom learning plan and the personalized attention that makes a difference in how students view math.

You can contact Reza via email at:
reza@EffortlessMath.com

Find Reza's professional profile at:
goo.gl/zoC9rJ

Contents

Chapter 1: Whole Numbers

Math Topics that you'll learn in this chapter:

- ✓ Rounding
- ✓ Whole Number Addition and Subtraction
- ✓ Whole Number Multiplication and Division
- ✓ Rounding and Estimates

Rounding

Step-by-step guide:

Rounding is putting a number up or down to the nearest whole number or the nearest hundred, etc.

- ✓ *First, find the place value you'll round to.*
- ✓ *Find the digit to the right of the place value you're rounding to. If it is 5 or bigger, add 1 to the place value you're rounding to and put zero for all digits on its right side. If the digit to the right of the place value is less than 5, keep the place value and put zero for all digits to the right.*

Examples:

1) Round 23 to the nearest ten.

The place value of ten is 2. The digit on the right side is 3 (which is less than 5). Keep 2 and put zero for the digit on the right side. The answer is 20. 23 rounded to the nearest ten is 20, because 23 is closer to 20 than to 30.

2) Round 475 to the nearest hundred.

475 rounded to the nearest hundred is 500, because the digit on the right side of hundred place is 7. Add 1 to 4 and put zeros for other digits. The answer is 500.

Round each number to the nearest ten.

1) $23 =$ ____
2) $16 =$ ____
3) $35 =$ ____
4) $48 =$ ____
5) $71 =$ ____
6) $99 =$ ____

Round each number to the nearest hundred.

7) $110 =$ ____
8) $119 =$ ____
9) $158 =$ ____
10) $109 =$ ____
11) $345 =$ ____
12) $670 =$ ____

Whole Number Addition and Subtraction

Step-by-step guide:

- ✓ *Line up the numbers.*
- ✓ *Start with the unit place. (ones place)*
- ✓ *Regroup if necessary.*
- ✓ *Add or subtract the tens place.*
- ✓ *Continue with other digits.*

Examples:

1) Find the sum. $485 + 245 = ?$

First line up the numbers: $\begin{array}{r} 485 \\ \underline{+\,245} \end{array}$ → Start with the unit place. (ones place) $5 + 5 = 10$,

Write 0 for ones place and keep 1, $\begin{array}{r} 1 \\ 485 \\ \underline{+\,245} \\ 0 \end{array}$, Add the tens place and the digit 1 we kept:

$1 + 8 + 4 = 13$, Write 3 and keep 1, $\begin{array}{r} 1\,1 \\ 485 \\ \underline{+\,245} \\ 30 \end{array}$

Continue with other digits → $1 + 4 + 2 = 7$ → $\begin{array}{r} 1\,1 \\ 485 \\ \underline{+\,245} \\ 730 \end{array}$

2) Find the difference. $576 - 353 = ?$

First line up the numbers: $\begin{array}{r} 576 \\ \underline{-\,353} \end{array}$, → Start with the unit place. $6 - 3 = 3$, $\begin{array}{r} 576 \\ \underline{-\,353} \\ 3 \end{array}$,

Subtract the tens place. $7 - 5 = 2$, $\begin{array}{r} 576 \\ \underline{-\,353} \\ 23 \end{array}$, Continue with other digits → $5 - 3 = 2$, $\begin{array}{r} 576 \\ \underline{-\,453} \\ 223 \end{array}$

Find the sum or difference.

1) $1{,}122 + 577 =$

2) $1{,}850 - 1{,}600 =$

3) $1{,}900 - 1{,}237 =$

4) $2{,}550 + 1{,}800 =$

5) $3{,}220 + 2{,}560 =$

6) $2{,}590 + 2{,}120 =$

7) $4{,}823 + 2{,}891 =$

8) $4{,}731 + 2{,}561 =$

Whole Number Multiplication

Step-by-step guide:

- ✓ Learn the times tables first! To solve multiplication problems fast, you need to memorize the times table. For example, 3 times 8 is 24 or 8 times 7 is 56.
- ✓ For multiplication, line up the numbers you are multiplying.
- ✓ Start with the ones place and regroup if necessary.
- ✓ Continue with other digits.

Examples:

1) Solve. $200 \times 10 = ?$

Line up the numbers: $\begin{array}{r} 200 \\ \underline{\times 10} \end{array}$, start with the ones place → $0 \times 200 = 0$, $\begin{array}{r} 200 \\ \underline{\times 10} \\ 0 \end{array}$, Continue with other digit which is 1. → $200 \times 1 = 200$, $\begin{array}{r} 200 \\ \underline{\times 10} \\ 2{,}000 \end{array}$

2) Solve. $120 \times 15 = ?$

Line up the numbers: $\begin{array}{r} 120 \\ \underline{\times 15} \end{array}$, start with the ones place → $5 \times 0 = 0$, $\begin{array}{r} 120 \\ \underline{\times 15} \\ 0 \end{array}$, $5 \times 2 = 10$, write 0 and keep 1. $\begin{array}{r} 120 \\ \underline{\times 15} \\ 00 \end{array}$, → $5 \times 1 = 5$, add 1 to 5, the answer is 6. $\begin{array}{r} 120 \\ \underline{\times 15} \\ 600 \end{array}$

Now, write 0 in the next line and multiply 120 by 1, using the same process. (Since 1 is in the tens place, we need to write 0 before doing the operation). The answer is 1,200.
Add 600 and 1,200. The answer is: $600 + 1{,}200 = 1{,}800$

Find the missing number.

1) $15 \times 6 =$ ______
2) $19 \times 7 =$ ______
3) $260 \times 9 =$ ______
4) $300 \times 12 =$ ______
5) $150 \times 50 =$ ______
6) $230 \times 20 =$ ______
7) $432 \times 25 =$ ______
8) $390 \times 34 =$ ______

Whole Number Division

Step-by-step guide:

Division: A typical division problem: Dividend ÷ Divisor = Quotient

- In division, we want to find how many times a number (divisor) is contained in another number (dividend). The result in a division problem is the quotient.
- ✓ First, write the problem in division format. (dividend is inside; divisor is outside)

Quotient

Divisor | Dividend

- ✓ Now, find how many times divisor goes into dividend. (if it is a big number, break the dividend into smaller numbers by choosing the appropriate number of digits from left. Start from the first digit on the left side of the divided and see if the divisor will go into it. If not, keep moving over one digit to the right in the dividend until you have a number the divisor will go into.
- ✓ Find number of times the divisor goes into the part of the dividend you chose.
- ✓ Write the answer above the digit in the dividend you are using and multiply it by the divisor and Write the product under the part of the dividend you are using, then subtract.
- ✓ Bring down the next digit in the dividend and repeat this process until you have nothing left to bring down.

Example: Solve. $234 \div 4 = ?$

- ✓ First, write the problem in division format. 4 | 234
- ✓ Start from left digit of the dividend. 4 doesn't go into 2. So, choose another digit of the dividend. It is 3.
- ✓ Now, find how many times 4 goes into 23. The answer is 5.
- ✓ Write 5 above the dividend part. 4 times 5 is 20. Write 20 below 23 and subtract. The answer is 3.
- ✓ Now bring down the next digit which is 4. How many times 4 goes into 34? The answer is 8. Write 8 above dividend. This is the final step since there is no other digit of the dividend to bring down. The final answer is 58 and the remainder is 2.

```
     5
4 | 234

     58
4 | 234
   - 20
    ---
     34
   - 32
    ---
      2
```

Solve.

1) $150 \div 5 =$ ______
2) $360 \div 6 =$ ______
3) $840 \div 7 =$ ______
4) $640 \div 8 =$ ______
5) $240 \div 6 =$ ______
6) $345 \div 8 =$ ______
7) $512 \div 13 =$ ______
8) $848 \div 25 =$ ______

Rounding and Estimates

Step-by-step guide:

Rounding and estimating are math strategies used for approximating a number. To estimate means to make a rough guess or calculation. To round means to simplify a known number by scaling it slightly up or down.

- ✓ To estimate a math operation, round the numbers.
- ✓ For 2-digit numbers, your usually can round to the nearest tens, for 3-digit numbers, round to nearest hundreds, etc.
- ✓ Find the answer.

Examples:

1) Estimate the sum by rounding each number to the nearest hundred. $\mathbf{145 + 489 = ?}$
   145 rounded to the nearest hundred is 100. 489 rounded to the nearest hundred is 500.
   Then: $100 + 500 = 600$
2) Estimate the result by rounding each number to the nearest ten. $\mathbf{55 - 43 = ?}$
   55 rounded to the nearest ten is 60. 43 rounded to the nearest ten is 40.
   Then: $55 - 40 = 15$

Estimate the sum by rounding each number to the nearest ten.

1) $12 + 26 =$ ______
2) $28 + 18 =$ ______
3) $31 + 37 =$ ______
4) $56 + 68 =$ ______
5) $232 + 191 =$ ______
6) $584 + 344 =$ ______

Estimate the product by rounding each number to the nearest ten.

7) $13 \times 18 =$ ______
8) $15 \times 25 =$ ______
9) $32 \times 27 =$ ______
10) $48 \times 23 =$ ______
11) $69 \times 35 =$ ______
12) $77 \times 54 =$ ______

Answers – Chapter 1

Rounding

1) 20
2) 20
3) 40
4) 50
5) 70
6) 100
7) 100
8) 100
9) 200
10) 100
11) 300
12) 700

Whole Number Addition and Subtraction

1) 1,699
2) 250
3) 663
4) 4,350
5) 5,780
6) 4,710
7) 7,714
8) 7,292

Whole Number Multiplication

1) 90
2) 133
3) 2,340
4) 3,600
5) 7,500
6) 4,600
7) 10,800
8) 13,260

Whole Number Division

1) 30
2) 60
3) 120
4) 80
5) 45
6) $43, r1$
7) $39, r5$
8) $33, r23$

Rounding and Estimates

1) 40
2) 50
3) 70
4) 130
5) 420
6) 900
7) 200
8) 600
9) 900
10) 1,000
11) 2,800
12) 4,000

Chapter 2: Fractions and Mixed Numbers

Math Topics that you'll learn in this chapter:

- ✓ Simplifying Fractions
- ✓ Adding and Subtracting Fractions
- ✓ Multiplying and Dividing Fractions
- ✓ Adding Mixed Numbers
- ✓ Subtracting Mixed Numbers
- ✓ Multiplying Mixed Numbers
- ✓ Dividing Mixed Numbers

Simplifying Fractions

Step-by-step guide:

- ✓ Evenly divide both the top and bottom of the fraction by $2, 3, 5, 7, \ldots$ etc.
- ✓ Continue until you can't go any further.

Examples:

1) Simplify $\frac{18}{24}$.

To simplify $\frac{18}{24}$, find a number that both 18 and 24 are divisible by. Both are divisible by 6.
Then: $\frac{18}{24} = \frac{18 \div 6}{24 \div 6} = \frac{3}{4}$

2) Simplify $\frac{72}{90}$.

To simplify $\frac{72}{90}$, find a number that both 72 and 90 are divisible by. Both are divisible by 9 and 18. Then: $\frac{72}{90} = \frac{72 \div 9}{90 \div 9} = \frac{8}{10}$, 8 and 10 are divisible by 2, then: $\frac{8}{10} = \frac{4}{5}$

or $\frac{72}{90} = \frac{72 \div 18}{90 \div 18} = \frac{4}{5}$

Simplify each fraction.

1) $\frac{8}{6} =$

2) $\frac{4}{16} =$

3) $\frac{13}{26} =$

4) $\frac{21}{28} =$

5) $\frac{30}{45} =$

6) $\frac{8}{48} =$

7) $\frac{15}{45} =$

8) $\frac{22}{26} =$

9) $\frac{28}{54} =$

10) $\frac{35}{75} =$

11) $\frac{49}{63} =$

12) $\frac{38}{50} =$

Adding and Subtracting Fractions

Step-by-step guide:

- ✓ For "like" fractions (fractions with the same denominator), add or subtract the numerators and write the answer over the common denominator.
- ✓ Find equivalent fractions with the same denominator before you can add or subtract fractions with different denominators.
- ✓ Adding and Subtracting with the same denominator:
  $\frac{a}{b}+\frac{c}{b}=\frac{a+c}{b}$, $\frac{a}{b}-\frac{c}{b}=\frac{a-c}{b}$
- ✓ Adding and Subtracting fractions with different denominators:
  $\frac{a}{b}+\frac{c}{d}=\frac{ad+\text{bc}}{bd}$, $\frac{a}{b}-\frac{c}{d}=\frac{ad-cb}{bd}$

Examples:

1) Subtract fractions. $\frac{2}{3}-\frac{1}{2}=$

   For "like" fractions, subtract the numerators and write the answer over the common denominator. then: $\frac{4}{6}-\frac{3}{6}=\frac{4-3}{6}=\frac{1}{6}$

2) Subtract fractions. $\frac{3}{7}+\frac{2}{3}=$

   For "unlike" fractions, find equivalent fractions with the same denominator before you can add or subtract fractions with different denominators. Use this formula: $\frac{a}{b}-\frac{c}{d}=\frac{ad-cb}{bd}$

   $\frac{3}{7}+\frac{2}{3}=\frac{(3)(3)+(2)(7)}{7\times 3}=\frac{9+14}{21}=\frac{23}{21}$

Find the sum or difference.

1) $\frac{4}{5}+\frac{2}{3}=$

2) $\frac{1}{4}+\frac{1}{3}=$

3) $\frac{3}{2}-\frac{1}{8}=$

4) $\frac{2}{5}-\frac{1}{3}=$

5) $\frac{3}{4}+\frac{5}{4}=$

6) $\frac{4}{7}+\frac{2}{3}=$

7) $\frac{4}{7}-\frac{1}{3}=$

8) $\frac{6}{7}-\frac{3}{5}=$

9) $\frac{3}{8}+\frac{1}{7}=$

Multiplying and Dividing Fractions

Step-by-step guide:

- ✓ Multiplying fractions: multiply the top numbers and multiply the bottom numbers.
- ✓ Dividing fractions: Keep, Change, Flip
- ✓ Keep first fraction, change division sign to multiplication, and flip the numerator and denominator of the second fraction. Then, solve!

Examples:

1) Multiplying fractions. $\frac{2}{5} \times \frac{3}{4} =$

Multiply the top numbers and multiply the bottom numbers.
$\frac{2}{5} \times \frac{3}{4} = \frac{2\times3}{5\times4} = \frac{6}{20}$, simplify: $\frac{6}{20} = \frac{6\div2}{20\div2} = \frac{3}{10}$

2) Dividing fractions. $\frac{1}{2} \div \frac{3}{5} =$

Keep first fraction, change division sign to multiplication, and flip the numerator and denominator of the second fraction. Then: $\frac{1}{2} \times \frac{5}{3} = \frac{1\times5}{2\times3} = \frac{5}{6}$

Find the answers.

1) $\frac{1}{3} \times \frac{5}{4} =$
2) $\frac{1}{7} \times \frac{3}{4} =$
3) $\frac{1}{5} \div \frac{1}{4} =$
4) $\frac{3}{4} \div \frac{2}{3} =$
5) $\frac{5}{6} \times \frac{1}{4} =$
6) $\frac{3}{8} \times \frac{5}{9} =$
7) $\frac{3}{8} \div \frac{1}{5} =$
8) $\frac{6}{15} \div \frac{1}{2} =$
9) $\frac{2}{7} \div \frac{6}{5} =$
10) $\frac{4}{7} \times \frac{8}{9} =$
11) $\frac{1}{16} \times \frac{4}{5} =$
12) $\frac{8}{15} \div \frac{6}{5} =$

Adding Mixed Numbers

Step-by-step guide:

Use the following steps for both adding and subtracting mixed numbers.

- ✓ Add whole numbers of the mixed numbers.
- ✓ Add the fractions of each mixed number.
- ✓ Find the Least Common Denominator (LCD) if necessary.
- ✓ Add whole numbers and fractions.
- ✓ Write your answer in lowest terms.

Examples:

1) Add mixed numbers. $1\frac{1}{2}+2\frac{2}{3}=$

Rewriting our equation with parts separated, $1+\frac{1}{2}+2+\frac{2}{3}$, Solving the whole number parts $1+2=3$, Solving the fraction parts $\frac{1}{2}+\frac{2}{3}$, and rewrite to solve with the equivalent fractions.

$\frac{3}{6}+\frac{4}{6}=\frac{7}{6}=1\frac{1}{6}$, then Combining the whole and fraction parts $3+1+\frac{1}{6}=4\frac{1}{6}$

2) Add mixed numbers. $2\frac{1}{4}+1\frac{2}{5}=$

Rewriting our equation with parts separated, $2+\frac{1}{4}+1+\frac{2}{5}$, Solving the whole number parts $2+1=3$, Solving the fraction parts $\frac{1}{4}+\frac{2}{5}$, and rewrite to solve with the equivalent fractions.

$\frac{5}{20}+\frac{8}{20}=\frac{13}{20}$, then Combining the whole and fraction parts $3+\frac{13}{20}=3\frac{13}{20}$

Find the sum.

1) $1\frac{1}{2}+2\frac{2}{3}=$

2) $2\frac{1}{3}+1\frac{1}{2}=$

3) $1\frac{3}{5}+2\frac{1}{4}=$

4) $3\frac{2}{5}+2\frac{1}{3}=$

5) $1\frac{2}{7}+1\frac{3}{4}=$

6) $3\frac{4}{5}+2\frac{2}{7}=$

7) $2\frac{1}{2}+7\frac{3}{8}=$

8) $2\frac{7}{8}+1\frac{1}{3}=$

9) $2\frac{4}{9}+6\frac{5}{12}=$

Subtract Mixed Numbers

Step-by-step guide:

Use the following steps for both adding and subtracting mixed numbers.

- ✓ Subtract the whole number of second mixed number from whole number of the first mixed number.
- ✓ Subtract the second fraction from the first one.
- ✓ Find the Least Common Denominator (LCD) if necessary.
- ✓ Add the result of whole numbers and fractions.
- ✓ Write your answer in lowest terms.

Examples:

1) Subtract. $2\frac{3}{5} - 1\frac{1}{3} =$

Rewriting our equation with parts separated, $2 + \frac{3}{5} - 1 - \frac{1}{3}$

Solving the whole number parts $2 - 1 = 1$, Solving the fraction parts, $\frac{3}{5} - \frac{1}{3} = \frac{9-5}{15} = \frac{4}{15}$

Combining the whole and fraction parts, $1 + \frac{4}{15} = 1\frac{4}{15}$

2) Subtract. $5\frac{5}{8} - 2\frac{1}{4} =$

Rewriting our equation with parts separated, $5 + \frac{5}{8} - 2 - \frac{1}{4}$

Solving the whole number parts $5 - 2 = 3$, Solving the fraction parts, $\frac{5}{8} - \frac{1}{4} = \frac{20-8}{32} = \frac{12}{32}$

Combining the whole and fraction parts, $3 + \frac{12}{32} = 3\frac{12}{32}$

Find the difference.

1) $1\frac{2}{3} - 1\frac{1}{2} =$	4) $4\frac{5}{6} - 2\frac{2}{3} =$	7) $4\frac{4}{9} - 2\frac{2}{3} =$
2) $2\frac{1}{4} - 1\frac{1}{5} =$	5) $5\frac{3}{5} - 2\frac{1}{4} =$	8) $9\frac{3}{10} - 4\frac{1}{3} =$
3) $3\frac{3}{4} - 2\frac{2}{3} =$	6) $6\frac{3}{7} - 1\frac{2}{5} =$	9) $12\frac{3}{8} - 8\frac{5}{12} =$

Multiplying Mixed Numbers

Step-by-step guide:

- ✓ Convert the mixed numbers to improper fractions. (improper fraction is a fraction in which the top number is bigger than bottom number)
- ✓ Multiply fractions and simplify if necessary.

$$a\frac{c}{b} = a + \frac{c}{b} = \frac{ab+c}{b}$$

Examples:

1) Multiply mixed numbers. $2\frac{1}{4} \times 3\frac{1}{2} =$

   Converting mixed numbers to fractions, $2\frac{1}{4} = \frac{9}{4}$ and $3\frac{1}{2} = \frac{7}{2}$.

   $\frac{9}{4} \times \frac{7}{2}$, Applying the fractions formula for multiplication, $\frac{9\times7}{4\times2} = \frac{63}{8} = 7\frac{7}{8}$

2) Multiply mixed numbers. $5\frac{2}{3} \times 3\frac{3}{4} =$

   Converting mixed numbers to fractions, $\frac{17}{3} \times \frac{15}{4}$, Applying the fractions formula for multiplication, $\frac{17\times15}{3\times4} = \frac{85}{4} = 21\frac{1}{4}$

Find the product.

1) $1\frac{1}{2} \times 2\frac{1}{4} =$
2) $1\frac{2}{3} \times 1\frac{3}{4} =$
3) $4\frac{2}{5} \times 2\frac{1}{2} =$
4) $3\frac{1}{6} \times 1\frac{2}{3} =$
5) $3\frac{2}{7} \times 2\frac{1}{5} =$
6) $4\frac{2}{3} \times 3\frac{1}{7} =$
7) $5\frac{3}{8} \times 2\frac{3}{4} =$
8) $3\frac{4}{7} \times 7\frac{2}{9} =$
9) $8\frac{3}{5} \times 4\frac{3}{8} =$
10) $6\frac{5}{7} \times 2\frac{5}{9} =$

Dividing Mixed Numbers

Step-by-step guide:

- ✓ Convert the mixed numbers to improper fractions.
- ✓ Divide fractions and simplify if necessary.

$a\frac{c}{b} = a + \frac{c}{b} = \frac{ab+c}{b}$

Examples:

1) Find the quotient. $2\frac{1}{3} \div 1\frac{1}{4} =$

Converting mixed numbers to fractions, $\frac{7}{3} \div \frac{5}{4}$, Applying the fractions formula for multiplication, $\frac{7\times4}{3\times5} = \frac{28}{15} = 1\frac{13}{15}$

2) Find the quotient. $2\frac{5}{6} \div 1\frac{2}{5} =$

Converting mixed numbers to fractions, $\frac{17}{6} \div \frac{7}{5}$, Applying the fractions formula for multiplication, $\frac{17\times5}{6\times7} = \frac{85}{42} = 2\frac{1}{42}$

Find the quotient.

1) $3\frac{1}{3} \div 2\frac{1}{2} =$

2) $2\frac{1}{2} \div 1\frac{1}{4} =$

3) $4\frac{3}{4} \div 2\frac{2}{3} =$

4) $3\frac{1}{6} \div 2\frac{2}{3} =$

5) $5\frac{1}{4} \div 2\frac{3}{5} =$

6) $2\frac{2}{7} \div 2\frac{1}{4} =$

7) $1\frac{4}{9} \div 2\frac{1}{3} =$

8) $7\frac{4}{5} \div 3\frac{2}{3} =$

9) $6\frac{3}{4} \div 2\frac{2}{5} =$

10) $8\frac{4}{7} \div 3\frac{5}{6} =$

Answers – Chapter 2

Simplifying Fractions

1) $\frac{4}{3}$
2) $\frac{1}{4}$
3) $\frac{1}{2}$
4) $\frac{3}{4}$
5) $\frac{2}{3}$
6) $\frac{1}{6}$
7) $\frac{1}{3}$
8) $\frac{11}{13}$
9) $\frac{14}{27}$
10) $\frac{7}{15}$
11) $\frac{7}{9}$
12) $\frac{19}{25}$

Adding and Subtracting Fractions

1) $\frac{22}{15}$
2) $\frac{7}{12}$
3) $\frac{11}{8}$
4) $\frac{1}{15}$
5) 2
6) $\frac{26}{21}$
7) $\frac{5}{21}$
8) $\frac{9}{35}$
9) $\frac{29}{56}$

Multiplying and Dividing Fractions

1) $\frac{5}{12}$
2) $\frac{3}{28}$
3) $\frac{4}{5}$
4) $\frac{9}{8}$
5) $\frac{5}{24}$
6) $\frac{5}{24}$
7) $\frac{15}{8}$
8) $\frac{4}{5}$
9) $\frac{5}{21}$
10) $\frac{32}{63}$
11) $\frac{1}{20}$
12) $\frac{4}{9}$

Adding Mixed Numbers

1) $4\frac{1}{6}$
2) $3\frac{5}{6}$
3) $3\frac{17}{20}$
4) $5\frac{11}{15}$
5) $3\frac{1}{28}$
6) $6\frac{3}{35}$
7) $9\frac{7}{8}$
8) $4\frac{5}{24}$
9) $8\frac{31}{36}$

Subtract Mixed Numbers

1) $\frac{1}{6}$
2) $1\frac{1}{20}$
3) $1\frac{1}{12}$
4) $2\frac{1}{6}$
5) $3\frac{7}{20}$
6) $5\frac{1}{35}$
7) $1\frac{7}{9}$
8) $4\frac{29}{30}$
9) $3\frac{23}{24}$

Multiplying Mixed Numbers

1) $3\frac{3}{8}$
2) $2\frac{11}{12}$
3) 11
4) $5\frac{5}{18}$
5) $7\frac{8}{35}$
6) $14\frac{2}{3}$
7) $14\frac{25}{32}$
8) $25\frac{50}{63}$
9) $37\frac{5}{8}$
10) $17\frac{10}{63}$

Dividing Mixed Numbers

1) $1\frac{1}{3}$
2) 2
3) $1\frac{25}{32}$
4) $1\frac{3}{16}$
5) $2\frac{1}{52}$
6) $1\frac{1}{63}$
7) $\frac{13}{21}$
8) $2\frac{7}{55}$
9) $2\frac{13}{16}$
10) $2\frac{38}{161}$

Chapter 3: Decimals

Math Topics that you'll learn in this chapter:

- ✓ Comparing Decimals
- ✓ Rounding Decimals
- ✓ Adding and Subtracting Decimals
- ✓ Multiplying and Dividing Decimals

Comparing Decimals

Step-by-step guide:

Decimals: is a fraction written in a special form. For example, instead of writing $\frac{1}{2}$ you can write $\mathbf{0.5}$.

For comparing decimals:

- ✓ Compare each digit of two decimals in the same place value.
- ✓ Start from left. Compare hundreds, tens, ones, tenth, hundredth, etc.
- ✓ To compare numbers, use these symbols:
- \- Equal to $=$, Less than $<$, Greater than $>$
  Greater than or equal $\geq$, Less than or equal $\leq$

Examples:

1) Compare 0.40 and 0.04.

   0.40 *is greater than* 0.04, because the tenth place of 0.40 is 4, but the tenth place of 0.04 is zero. Then: $0.40 > 0.04$

2) Compare 0.0912 and 0.912.

   0.912 *is greater than* 0.0912, because the tenth place of 0.912 is 9, but the tenth place of 0.0912 is zero. Then: $0.0912 < 0.912$

Write the correct comparison symbol (>, < or =).

1) $0.70 \square 0.070$

2) $0.018 \square 0.18$

3) $1.050 \square 1.05$

4) $2.75 \square 2.07$

5) $1.05 \square 0.550$

6) $4.05 \square 4.5$

7) $7.05 \square 7.050$

8) $12.02 \square 12.1$

9) $8.45 \square 8.125$

10) $0.813 \square 0.0813$

11) $14.15 \square 14.150$

12) $0.678 \square 0.687$

Rounding Decimals

Step-by-step guide:

- ✓ We can round decimals to a certain accuracy or number of decimal places. This is used to make calculation easier to do and results easier to understand, when exact values are not too important.
- ✓ First, you'll need to remember your place values: For example:

$$12.4567$$

1: tens	2: ones	4: tenths
5: hundredths	6: thousandths	7: tens thousandths

- ✓ To round a decimal, find the place value you'll round to.
- ✓ Find the digit to the right of the place value you're rounding to. If it is 5 or bigger, add 1 to the place value you're rounding to and remove all digits on its right side. If the digit to the right of the place value is less than 5, keep the place value and remove all digits on the right.

Examples:

1) Round 1.9278 to the thousandth place value.

First look at the next place value to the right, (tens thousandths). It's 8 and it is greater than 5. Thus add 1 to the digit in the thousandth place.

Thousandth place is 7. → $7 + 1 = 8$, then, the answer is 1.928

2) 9.4126 rounded to the nearest hundredth.

First look at the next place value to the right of thousandths. It's 2 and it is less than 5, thus remove all the digits to the right. Then, the answer is 9.41.

Round each decimal to the nearest whole number.

1) 12.22
2) 9.5
3) 11.45
4) 24.5
5) 9.95
6) 77.8

Round each decimal to the nearest tenth.

7) 14.352
8) 10.569
9) 34.428
10) 67.249
11) 1.7925
12) 23.319

Adding and Subtracting Decimals

Step-by-step guide:

- ✓ Line up the numbers.
- ✓ Add zeros to have same number of digits for both numbers if necessary.
- ✓ Add or subtract using column addition or subtraction.

Examples:

1) Add. $1.5 + 2.14 =$

First line up the numbers: $\begin{array}{r} 1.5 \\ \underline{+\,2.14} \\ \end{array}$ → Add zeros to have same number of digits for both numbers. $\begin{array}{r} 1.50 \\ \underline{+\,2.14} \\ \end{array}$, Start with the hundredths place. $0 + 4 = 4$, $\begin{array}{r} 1.50 \\ \underline{+\,2.14} \\ 4 \end{array}$, Continue with tenths place. $5 + 1 = 6$, $\begin{array}{r} 1.50 \\ \underline{+\,2.14} \\ .64 \end{array}$. Add the ones place. $2 + 1 = 3$, $\begin{array}{r} 1.50 \\ \underline{+\,2.14} \\ 3.64 \end{array}$

2) Subtract decimals. $2.56 - 1.15 =$ $\begin{array}{r} 2.56 \\ \underline{-\,1.15} \\ \end{array}$

Start with the hundredths place. $6 - 5 = 1$, $\begin{array}{r} 2.56 \\ \underline{-\,1.15} \\ 1 \end{array}$, continue with tenths place. $5 - 1 = 4$ $\begin{array}{r} 2.56 \\ \underline{-\,1.15} \\ .41 \end{array}$, subtract the ones place. $2 - 1 = 1$, $\begin{array}{r} 2.56 \\ \underline{-\,1.15} \\ 1.41 \end{array}$.

Find the sum or difference.

1) $18.24 - 12.20 =$
2) $21.50 + 17.77 =$
3) $13.98 + 11.78 =$
4) $66.34 - 48.50 =$
5) $53.12 + 15.25 =$
6) $78.90 - 23.61 =$
7) $82.24 - 65.55 =$
8) $93.75 + 82.63 =$

Multiplying and Dividing Decimals

Step-by-step guide:

For Multiplication:

- ✓ Ignore the decimal point and set up and multiply the numbers as you do with whole numbers.
  Count the total number of decimal places in both of the factors.
  Place the decimal point in the product.
  For Division:
- ✓ If the divisor is not a whole number, move decimal point to right to make it a whole number. Do the same for dividend.
- ✓ Divide similar to whole numbers.

Examples:

1) Find the product. $0.60 \times 0.20 =$

Set up and multiply the numbers as you do with whole numbers. Line up the numbers: $\frac{\begin{array}{r}60\\ \times 20\end{array}}{}$, Start with the ones place $\rightarrow 60 \times 0 = 0$, $\frac{\begin{array}{r}60\\ \times 20\end{array}}{0}$, Continue with other digits $\rightarrow 60 \times 2 = 120$, $\frac{\begin{array}{r}60\\ \times 20\end{array}}{1{,}200}$, Count the total number of decimal places in both of the factors. (4). Then Place the decimal point in the product. Then: $\frac{\begin{array}{r}0.60\\ \times 0.20\end{array}}{0.1200} \rightarrow 0.60 \times 0.20 = 0.12$

2) Find the quotient. $1.40 \div 0.2 =$

The divisor is not a whole number. Multiply it by 10 to get 2. Do the same for the dividend to get 14. Now, divide: $14 \div 2 = 7$. The answer is 7.

Find the product and quotient.

1) $0.2 \times 0.5 =$

2) $1.5 \times 0.8 =$

3) $0.25 \times 0.5 =$

4) $0.15 \times 0.30 =$

5) $1.12 \times 0.4 =$

6) $0.34 \times 0.5 =$

7) $2.25 \div 0.5 =$

8) $62.2 \div 1{,}000 =$

9) $8.42 \div 2 =$

10) $8.6 \div 0.4 =$

11) $42.6 \div 0.2 =$

12) $86.5 \div 5 =$

Answers – Chapter 3

Comparing Decimals

1) $>$
2) $<$
3) $=$
4) $>$
5) $>$
6) $<$
7) $=$
8) $<$
9) $>$
10) $>$
11) $=$
12) $<$

Rounding Decimals

1) 12
2) 10
3) 11
4) 25
5) 10
6) 78
7) 14.4
8) 10.6
9) 34.4
10) 67.2
11) 1.8
12) 23.3

Adding and Subtracting Decimals

1) 6.04
2) 39.27
3) 25.76
4) 17.84
5) 68.37
6) 55.29
7) 16.69
8) 176.38

Multiplying and Dividing Decimals

1) 0.1
2) 1.2
3) 0.125
4) 0.045
5) 0.448
6) 0.17
7) 4.5
8) 0.0622
9) 4.21
10) 21.5
11) 213
12) 17.3

Chapter 4: Factoring Numbers

Math Topics that you'll learn in this chapter:

- ✓ Factoring Numbers
- ✓ Greatest Common Factor
- ✓ Least Common Multiple

Factoring Numbers

Step-by-step guide:

- ✓ Factoring numbers means to break the numbers into their prime factors.
- ✓ First few prime numbers: $2, 3, 5, 7, 11, 13, 17, 19$

Examples:

1) List all positive factors of 8.

Write the upside-down division:
The second column is the answer.
Then: $8 = 2 \times 2 \times 2$ or $8 = 2^3$

8	2
4	2
2	2
1	

2) List all positive factors of 24.

Write the upside-down division:
The second column is the answer.
Then: $24 = 2 \times 2 \times 2 \times 3$
or $20 = 2^3 \times 3$

24	2
12	2
6	2
3	3
1	

List all positive factors of each number.

1) 4
2) 6
3) 9
4) 12
5) 16
6) 18
7) 24
8) 28
9) 36
10) 38
11) 42
12) 56

Greatest Common Factor

Step-by-step guide:

- ✓ List the prime factors of each number.
- ✓ Multiply common prime factors.
- ✓ If there are no common prime factors, the GCF is 1.

Examples:

1) Find the GCF for 8 and 12.

   The factors of 8 are: $\{1, 2, 4, 8\}$

   The factors of 12 are: $\{1, 2, 3, 4, 6, 12\}$

   There is 4 in common,

   Then the greatest common factor is: 4.

2) Find the GCF for 14 and 18.

   The factors of 8 are: $\{1, 2, 7, 14\}$

   The factors of 20 are: $\{1, 2, 3, 6, 9, 18\}$

   There is 2 in common.

   Then the greatest common factor is: 2.

Find the GCF for each number pair.

1) 6, 2
2) 4, 8
3) 5, 10
4) 8,12
5) 4, 10
6) 6, 18
7) 9, 24
8) 16, 14
9) 15, 12
10) 14, 20
11) 12, 26
12) 22, 32

Least Common Multiple

Step-by-step guide:

- ✓ Least Common Multiple is the smallest multiple that 2 or more numbers have in common.
- ✓ How to find LCM: list out all the multiples of each number and then find the first one they have in common,

Examples:

1) Find the LCM for 8 and 6.

   Multiples of 8: $8, 16, 24, \ldots$

   Multiples of 6: $6, 12, 18, 24, \ldots$

   $LCM = 24$

2) Find the LCM for 4 and 12.

   Multiples of 4: $4, 8, 12, 16, 20, \ldots$

   Multiples of 12: $12, 24, 36, 48$

   $LCM = 12$

Find the LCM for each number pair.

1) $2, 4$
2) $3, 6$
3) $6, 8$
4) $7, 12$
5) $8, 16$
6) $12, 8$
7) $4, 12$
8) $5, 20$
9) $6, 22$
10) $14, 28$
11) $16, 18$
12) $24, 32$

Answers – Chapter 4

Factoring Numbers

1) 2×2
2) 2×3
3) 3×3
4) $2 \times 2 \times 3$
5) $2 \times 2 \times 2 \times 2$
6) $2 \times 3 \times 3$
7) $2 \times 2 \times 2 \times 3$
8) $2 \times 2 \times 7$
9) $2 \times 2 \times 3 \times 3$
10) 2×19
11) $2 \times 3 \times 7$
12) $2 \times 2 \times 2 \times 7$

Greatest Common Factor

1) 2
2) 4
3) 5
4) 4
5) 2
6) 6
7) 3
8) 2
9) 3
10) 2
11) 2
12) 2

Least Common Multiple

1) 4
2) 6
3) 24
4) 84
5) 16
6) 24
7) 12
8) 20
9) 66
10) 28
11) 144
12) 96

Chapter 5: Integers and Order of Operations

Math Topics that you'll learn in this chapter:

- ✓ Adding and Subtracting Integers
- ✓ Multiplying and Dividing Integers
- ✓ Ordering Integers and Numbers
- ✓ Order of Operations
- ✓ Integers and Absolute Value

Adding and Subtracting Integers

Step-by-step guide:

- ✓ Integers includes: zero, counting numbers, and the negative of the counting numbers. $\{\dots, -3, -2, -1, 0, 1, 2, 3, \dots\}$
- ✓ Add a positive integer by moving to the right on the number line.
- ✓ Add a negative integer by moving to the left on the number line.
- ✓ Subtract an integer by adding its opposite.

Examples:

1) Solve. $(-2) - (-6) =$

   Keep the first number, and convert the sign of the second number to it's opposite. (change subtraction into addition. Then: $(-2) + 6 = 4$

2) Solve. $8 + (12 - 20) =$

   First subtract the numbers in brackets, $12 - 20 = -8$

   Then: $8 + (-8) =$ → change addition into subtraction: $8 - 8 = 0$

Find each sum or difference.

1) $-(2) + 9 =$

2) $(-4) + (-8) =$

3) $12 + (-18) =$

4) $13 + (-22) =$

5) $2 + (-9) + 3 =$

6) $(-18) + (-4) + 2 =$

7) $4 + (-2) - (-8) =$

8) $5 - (-20 - 12) =$

9) $(-4 + 2) - 6 =$

10) $10 - (-6 + 5) =$

11) $15 - (5 - 3) =$

12) $-(22) - (-13) + 4 =$

Multiplying and Dividing Integers

Step-by-step guide:

Use these rules for multiplying and dividing integers:

- ✓ (negative) × (negative) = positive
- ✓ (negative) ÷ (negative) = positive
- ✓ (negative) × (positive) = negative
- ✓ (negative) ÷ (positive) = negative
- ✓ (positive) × (positive) = positive

Examples:

1) Solve. $3 \times (12 - 14) =$

First subtract the numbers in brackets, $12 - 14 = -2 \rightarrow (3) \times (-2) =$

Now use this formula: (negative) × (positive) = negative
$(3) \times (-2) = -6$

2) Solve. $(-8) + (12 \div 4) =$

First divided 48 by 6 , the numbers in brackets, $12 \div 4 = 3$

$= (-8) + (3) = -8 + 3 = -5$

Find each product or quotient.

1) $(-2) \times (9) =$

2) $(-12) \times 3 =$

3) $(-5) \times (-8) =$

4) $(-3) \times (-10) =$

5) $(-4) \times (-3) \times 2 =$

6) $(18 - 3) \times (-5) =$

7) $(16 - 4) \div (-4) =$

8) $(-15) \div (-3) =$

9) $(-48) \div (-6) =$

10) $56 \div (-8) =$

11) $(-121) \div 11 =$

12) $(-128) \div (-4) =$

Ordering Integers and Numbers

Step-by-step guide:

- ✓ When using a number line, numbers increase as you move to the right.
- ✓ When comparing two numbers, think about their position on number line. If one number is on the right side of another number, it is a bigger number. For example, -3 is bigger than -5 because it is on the right side of -5 on number line.

Examples:

1) Order this set of integers from least to greatest. $-4, -1, -5, 4, 2, 7$
The smallest number is -5 and the largest number is 7.

Now compare the integers and order them from least to greatest:
$-5 < -4 < -1 < 2 < 4 < 7$

2) Order each set of integers from greatest to least. $3, -2, -1, 6, -9, 8$
The largest number is 8 and the smallest number is -9.

Now compare the integers and order them from greatest to least:
$8 > 6 > 3 > -1 > -2 > -9$

Order each set of integers from least to greatest.

1) $6, -8, -5, 0, 2$ ____, ____, ____, ____, ____, ____
2) $-3, -10, 4, 11, 8$ ____, ____, ____, ____, ____, ____
3) $17, -11, -18, 20, -19$ ____, ____, ____, ____, ____, ____
4) $-14, -24, 17, -6, 31$ ____, ____, ____, ____, ____, ____

Order each set of integers from greatest to least.

5) $10, 15, -8, -11, -5$ ____, ____, ____, ____, ____, ____
6) $22, 30, -13, -19, 38$ ____, ____, ____, ____, ____, ____
7) $44, -20, -17, 54, -4$ ____, ____, ____, ____, ____, ____
8) $67, 80, -13, -9, 93$ ____, ____, ____, ____, ____, ____

Order of Operations

Step-by-step guide:

When there is more than one math operation, use PEMDAS:

- ✓ Parentheses
- ✓ Exponents
- ✓ Multiplication and Division (from left to right)
- ✓ Addition and Subtraction (from left to right)

Examples:

1) Solve. $(2+4) \div (2^2 \div 4) =$

   First simplify inside parentheses: $(6) \div (4 \div 4) = (6) \div (1) =$
   Then: $(6) \div (1) = 6$

2) Solve. $(9 \times 6) - (10 - 6) =$

   First simplify inside parentheses: $(9 \times 6) - (10 - 6) = (54) - (4) =$

   Then: $(54) - (4) = 50$

Evaluate each expression.

1) $12 + (3 \times 2) =$
2) $8 - (4 \times 5) =$
3) $(8 \times 2) + 14 =$
4) $(10 - 6) - (4 \times 3) =$
5) $15 + (12 \div 2) =$
6) $(24 \times 3) \div 4 =$
7) $(28 \div 2) \times (-4) =$
8) $(2 \times 6) + (14 - 8) =$
9) $45 + (4 \times 2) + 12 =$
10) $(10 \times 5) \div (4 + 1) =$
11) $(-6) + (8 \times 6) + 10 =$
12) $(12 \times 4) - (56 \div 4) =$

Integers and Absolute Value

Step-by-step guide:

- ✓ To find an absolute value of a number, just find its distance from 0 on number line! For example, the distance of 12 and -12 from zero on number line is 12!

Examples:

1) Solve. $|8-2| \times \frac{|-4\times6|}{3} =$

First solve $|8-2|$, →$|8-2| = |6|$, the absolute value of 6 is 6, $|6| = 6$

$6 \times \frac{|-4\times6|}{3} =$

Now solve $|-4 \times 6|$, → $|-4 \times 6| = |-24|$, the absolute value of -24 is 24, $|-24| = 24$

Then: $6 \times \frac{24}{3} = \ 6 \times 8 = 48$

2) Solve. $\frac{|-12|}{3} \times |9-4| =$

First find $|-12|$, →the absolute value of -12 is 12, then: $|-12| = 12$

$\frac{12}{3} \times |9-4| =$

Next, solve $|9-4|$, → $|9-4| = |-5|$, the absolute value of -5 is 5. $|-5| = 5$

Then: $\frac{12}{3} \times 5 = 4 \times 5 = 20$

✍ ***Evaluate the value.***

1) $2 - |4-10| - |8| =$

2) $|7| - \frac{|-14|}{2} =$

3) $\frac{|-18|}{3} \times |-4| =$

4) $\frac{|6\times-4|}{2} \times \frac{|-28|}{4} =$

5) $|12 \times -2| + \frac{|-56|}{7} =$

6) $\frac{|-40|}{4} \times \frac{|-66|}{11} =$

7) $|-25+3| \times \frac{|-8\times5|}{2}$

8) $\frac{|20\times-3|}{2} \times |-14| =$

Answers – Chapter 5

Adding and Subtracting Integers

1) 7
2) -12
3) -6
4) -9
5) -4
6) -20
7) 10
8) 37
9) -8
10) 11
11) 13
12) -5

Multiplying and Dividing Integers

1) -18
2) -36
3) 40
4) 30
5) 24
6) -75
7) -3
8) 5
9) 8
10) -7
11) -11
12) 32

Ordering Integers and Numbers

1) $-8, -5, 0, 2, 6$
2) $-10, -3, 4, 8, 11$
3) $-19, -18, -11, 17, 20$
4) $-24, -14, -6, 17, 31$
5) $15, 10, -5, -8, -11$
6) $38, 30, 22, -13, -19$
7) $54, 44, -4, -17, -20$
8) $93, 80, 67, -9, -13$

Order of Operations

1) 18
2) -12
3) 30
4) -8
5) 21
6) 18
7) -56
8) 18
9) 65
10) 10
11) 52
12) 34

Integers and Absolute Value

1) -12
2) 0
3) 24
4) 84
5) 32
6) 60
7) 440
8) 420

Chapter 6:

Ratios

Math Topics that you'll learn in this chapter:

- ✓ Simplifying Ratios
- ✓ Proportional Ratios
- ✓ Create a Proportion
- ✓ Similarity and Ratios
- ✓ Simple Interest

Simplifying Ratios

Step-by-step guide:

- ✓ Ratios are used to make comparisons between two numbers.
- ✓ Ratios can be written as a fraction, using the word "to", or with a colon.
- ✓ You can calculate equivalent ratios by multiplying or dividing both sides of the ratio by the same number.

Examples:

1) Simplify. $4:2 =$

Both numbers 4 and 2 are divisible by 2 , $\Rightarrow 4 \div 2 = 2, 2 \div 2 = 1,$

Then: $4:2 = 2:1$

2) Simplify. $\frac{14}{24} =$

Both numbers 14 and 24 are divisible by 2, $\Rightarrow\ 14 \div 2 = 7, 24 \div 2 = 12,$

Then: $\frac{14}{24} = \frac{7}{12}$

Reduce each ratio.

1) $4:8 =$ ___:___

2) $5:10 =$ ___:___

3) $3:9 =$ ___:___

4) $8:6 =$ ___:___

5) $6:14 =$ ___:___

6) $5:25 =$ ___:___

7) $16:18 =$ ___:___

8) $30:40 =$ ___:___

9) $15:50 =$ ___:___

10) $14:18 =$ ___:___

11) $15:27 =$ ___:___

12) $48:24 =$ ___:___

Proportional Ratios

Step-by-step guide:

- ✓ A proportion means that two ratios are equal. It can be written in two ways: $\frac{a}{b} = \frac{c}{d}$, $a : b = c : d$
- ✓ The proportion $\frac{a}{b} = \frac{c}{d}$ can be written as: $a \times d = c \times b$

Examples:

1) Solve this proportion for x. $\frac{2}{4} = \frac{3}{x}$

   Use cross multiplication: $\frac{2}{4} = \frac{3}{x} \Rightarrow 2 \times x = 3 \times 4 \Rightarrow 2x = 12$

   Divide to find x: $x = \frac{12}{2} \Rightarrow x = 6$

2) If a box contains red and blue balls in ratio of $2:5$ red to blue, how many red balls are there if 60 blue balls are in the box?

   Write a proportion and solve. $\frac{2}{5} = \frac{x}{60}$

   Use cross multiplication: $2 \times 60 = 5 \times x \Rightarrow 120 = 5x$

   Divide to find x: $x = \frac{120}{5} \Rightarrow x = 24$

Solve each proportion.

1) $\frac{2}{4} = \frac{8}{x}, x =$ ____
2) $\frac{1}{2} = \frac{6}{x}, x =$ ____
3) $\frac{2}{3} = \frac{12}{x}, x =$ ____
4) $\frac{1}{4} = \frac{x}{20}, x =$ ____
5) $\frac{3}{4} = \frac{x}{8}, x =$ ____
6) $\frac{1}{4} = \frac{18}{x}, x =$ ____
7) $\frac{5}{8} = \frac{10}{x}, x =$ ____
8) $\frac{6}{9} = \frac{24}{x}, x =$ ____
9) $\frac{4}{6} = \frac{x}{18}, x =$ ____
10) $\frac{5}{8} = \frac{x}{112}, x =$ ____
11) $\frac{3}{18} = \frac{x}{120}, x =$ ____
12) $\frac{12}{18} = \frac{x}{96}, x =$ ____

Create a Proportion

Step-by-step guide:

- ✓ A proportion contains two equal fractions! A proportion simply means that two fractions are equal.
- ✓ To create a proportion, simply find (or create) two equal fractions.

Examples:

1) Express ratios as a Proportion.
180 miles on 9 gallons of gas, how many miles on 1 gallon of gas?

First create a fraction: $\frac{180\ miles}{9\ gallons}$, and divide: $180 \div 9 = 20$

Then: 20 miles per gallon

2) State if this pair of ratios form a proportion. $\frac{2}{3}\ and\ \frac{12}{30}$

Use cross multiplication: $\frac{2}{3} = \frac{12}{30} \rightarrow 2 \times 30 = 12 \times 3 \rightarrow 60 = 36$, which is not correct.
Therefore, this pair of ratios doesn't form a proportion.

State if each pair of ratios form a proportion.

1) $\frac{2}{10}\ and\ \frac{4}{20}$

2) $\frac{1}{2}\ and\ \frac{15}{25}$

3) $\frac{4}{9}\ and\ \frac{40}{81}$

4) $\frac{6}{11}\ and\ \frac{42}{77}$

5) $\frac{1}{6}\ and\ \frac{8}{48}$

6) $\frac{5}{6}\ and\ \frac{35}{42}$

7) $\frac{3}{7}\ and\ \frac{27}{72}$

8) $\frac{2}{5}\ and\ \frac{16}{45}$

9) $\frac{6}{17}\ and\ \frac{36}{85}$

10) $\frac{2}{7}\ and\ \frac{24}{86}$

11) $\frac{13}{21}\ and\ \frac{182}{294}$

12) $\frac{12}{19}\ and\ \frac{156}{247}$

Similarity and Ratios

Step-by-step guide:

✓ Two or more figures are similar if the corresponding angles are equal, and the corresponding sides are in proportion.

Examples:

1) A girl $180\ cm$ tall, stands $340\ cm$ from a lamp post at night. Her shadow from the light is $80\ cm$ long. How high is the lamp post?

Write the proportion and solve for missing side.

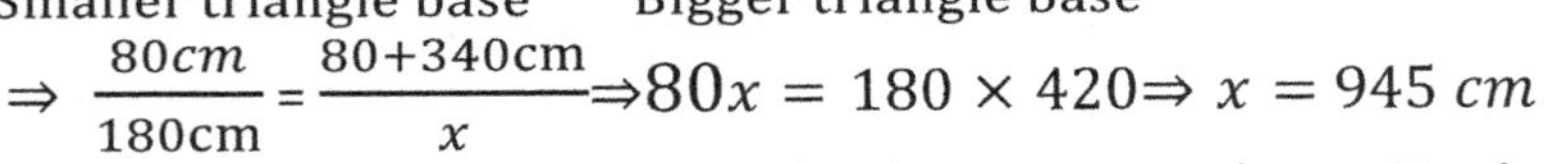

$$\frac{\text{Smaller triangle height}}{\text{Smaller triangle base}} = \frac{\text{Bigger triangle height}}{\text{Bigger triangle base}}$$

$$\Rightarrow \frac{80cm}{180\text{cm}} = \frac{80+340\text{cm}}{x} \Rightarrow 80x = 180 \times 420 \Rightarrow x = 945\ cm$$

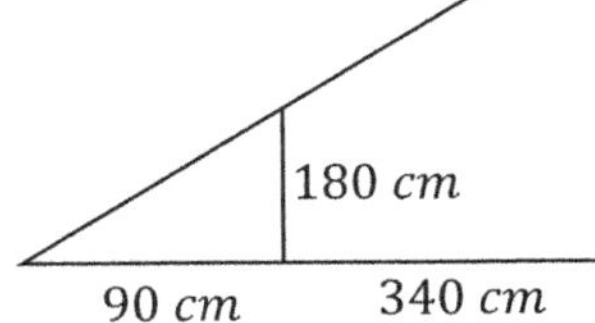

2) A tree $20\ feet$ tall casts a shadow $14\ feet$ long. Jack is $10\ feet$ tall. How long is Jack's shadow?

Write a proportion and solve for the missing number.

$$\frac{20}{14} = \frac{10}{x} \rightarrow 20x = 10 \times 14$$

$$20x = 140 \rightarrow x = \frac{140}{20} = 7$$

Each pair of figures is similar. Find the missing side.

1)

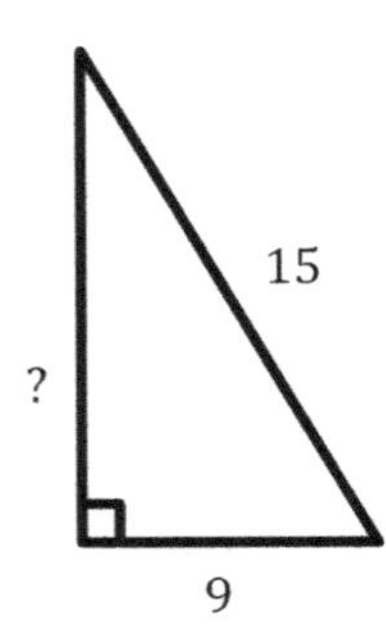

3, 5, 4

2)

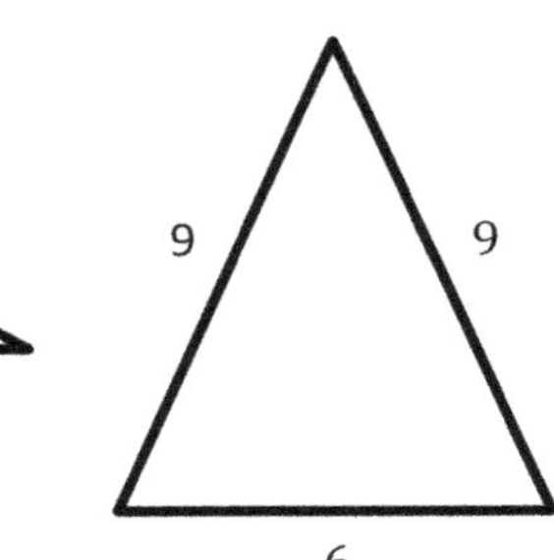

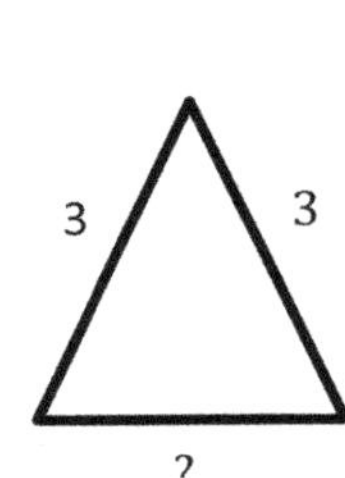

3)

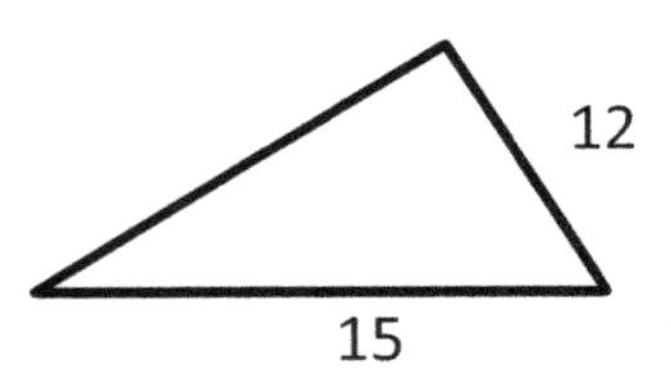

4, ?

4)

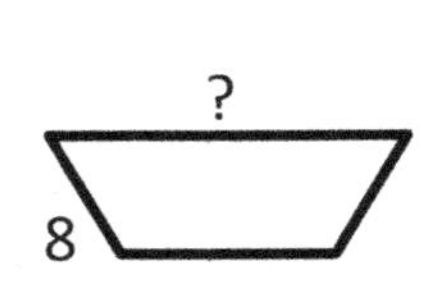

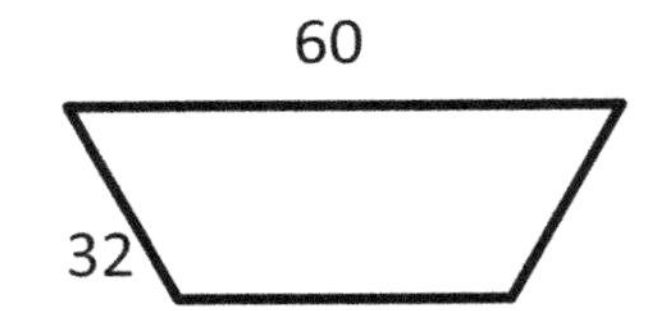

Simple Interest

Step-by-step guide:

✓ Simple Interest: The charge for borrowing money or the return for lending it. To solve a simple interest problem, use this formula:
Interest = principal x rate x time ⇒ $I = p \times r \times t$

Examples:

1) Find simple interest for \$450 investment at 7% for 8 years.

Use Interest formula: $I = prt$

$P = \$450$, $r = 7\% = \frac{7}{100} = 0.07$ and $t = 8$

Then: $I = 450 \times 0.07 \times 8 = \$252$

2) Find simple interest for \$5,200 at 4% for 3 years.

Use Interest formula: $I = prt$

$P = \$5{,}200$, $r = 4\% = \frac{4}{100} = 0.04$ and $t = 3$

Then: $I = 5{,}200 \times 0.04 \times 3 = \$624$

Determine the simple interest for these loans.

1) \$840 at 6% for 4 years. \$ ________
2) \$2,500 at 2% for 8 years. \$ ________
3) \$1,200 at 4% for 5 years. \$ ________
4) \$4,000 at 1.5% for 3 years. \$ ________
5) \$5,300 at 3% for 2 years. \$ ________
6) \$1,200 at 5.5% for 4 years. \$ ________
7) \$1,800 at 5% for 6 months. \$ ________
8) \$20,000 at 2.5% for 7 years. \$ ________

Answers – Chapter 6

Simplifying Ratios

1) 1: 2
2) 1: 2
3) 1: 3
4) 4: 3
5) 3: 7
6) 1: 5
7) 8: 9
8) 3: 4
9) 3: 10
10) 7: 9
11) 5: 9
12) 2: 1

Proportional Ratios

1) 16
2) 12
3) 18
4) 5
5) 6
6) 72
7) 16
8) 36
9) 12
10) 70
11) 20
12) 96

Create a Proportion

1) Yes
2) No
3) No
4) Yes
5) Yes
6) Yes
7) Yes
8) *No*
9) No
10) No
11) Yes
12) Yes

Similarity and ratios

1) 12
2) 2
3) 5
4) 15

Simple Interest

1) $201.60
2) $400
3) $240
4) $180
5) $318
6) $264
7) $45
8) $3,500

Chapter 7: Percentage

Math Topics that you'll learn in this chapter:

- ✓ Percentage Calculations
- ✓ Percent Problems
- ✓ Percent of Increase and Decrease
- ✓ Discount, Tax and Tip

Percentage Calculations

Step-by-step guide:

- ✓ Percent is a ratio of a number and 100. It always has the same denominator, 100. Percent symbol is %.
- ✓ Percent is another way to write decimals or fractions. For example:

$$40\% = 0.40 = \frac{40}{100} = \frac{2}{5}$$

- ✓ Use the following formula to find part, whole, or percent:

$$\text{part} = \frac{\text{percent}}{100} \times \text{ whole}$$

Examples:

1) What is 15% of 50? Use the following formula: $\text{part} = \frac{\text{percent}}{100} \times \text{whole}$

$\text{part} = \frac{15}{100} \times 50 \rightarrow \text{part} = \frac{15\times50}{100} \rightarrow \text{part} = \frac{75}{10} \rightarrow \text{part} = 7.5$

2) What is 30% of 35? Use the percent formula: $part = \frac{percent}{100} \times whole$

$\text{part} = \frac{30}{100} \times 35 \rightarrow \text{part} = \frac{105}{10} \rightarrow \text{part} = 10.5$

Calculate the given percent of each value.

1) 10% of 100 = ____
2) 50% of 40 = ____
3) 20% of 50 = ____
4) 30% of 70 = ____
5) 45% of 20 = ____
6) 50% of 80 = ____
7) 30% of 100 = ____
8) 15% of 60 = ____
9) 40% of 90 = ____
10) 29% of 86 = ____
11) 33% of 54 = ____
12) 71% of 112 = ____

Percent Problems

Step-by-step guide:

- ✓ In each percent problem, we are looking for the base, or part or the percent.
- ✓ Use the following equations to find each missing section.
  - Base = Part ÷ Percent
  - Part = Percent × Base
  - Percent = Part ÷ Base

Examples:

1) 2.5 is what percent of 20?

In this problem, we are looking for the percent. Use the following equation:

$$Percent = Part \div Base \rightarrow Percent = 2.5 \div 20 = 0.125 = 12.5\%$$

2) 40 is 10% of what number?

Use the following formula: $Base = Part \div Percent \rightarrow Base = 40 \div 0.10 = 400$

40 is 10% of 400.

Solve each problem.

1) 20 is what percent of 200? ____%
2) 40 is what percent of 50? ____%
3) 30 is 15 percent of what number? ____
4) 18 is 6 percent of what? ____
5) 20 is what percent of 50? ____%
6) 18 is what percent of 90? ____%
7) 25 is what percent of 80? ____%
8) 60 is what percent of 300? ____%
9) 50 is 20 percent of what number? ____
10) 68 *is* 16 *percent of what?* ___
11) 15 *is* 25 *percent of what?* ___
12) 80 *is* 25 *percent of what?* ___

Percent of Increase and Decrease

Step-by-step guide:

To find the percentage of increase or decrease:

- ✓ New Number - Original Number
- ✓ The result ÷ Original Number × 100
- ✓ If your answer is a negative number, then this is a percentage decrease. If it is positive, then this is a percent of increase.

Examples:

1) Increased by 20%, the numbers 30 becomes:

First find 20% of 30 → $\frac{20}{100} \times 30 = \frac{20 \times 30}{100} = 6$

Then: $30 + 6 = 36$

2) The price of a shirt increases from $\$10$ to $\$15$. What is the percent increase?
First: $15 - 10 = 5$
5 is the result. Then: $5 \div 10 = \frac{5}{10} = 0.5 = 50\%$

Solve each percent of change word problem.

1) Bob got a raise, and his hourly wage increased from $\$20$ to $\$25$. What is the percent increase? ______ %
2) The price of a pair of shoes increases from $\$18$ to $\$27$. What is the percent increase? ____ %
3) At a coffeeshop, the price of a cup of coffee increased from $\$1.50$ to $\$1.80$. What is the percent increase in the cost of the coffee? ______ %
4) $4\ cm$ are cut from a $20\ cm$ board. What is the percent decrease in length? ______ %
5) In a class, the number of students has been increased from 25 to 29. What is the percent increase? ______ %
6) The price of gasoline rose from $\$2.60$ to $\$2.86$ in one month. By what percent did the gas price rise? ______ %
7) A shirt was originally priced at $\$48$. It went on sale for $\$38.40$. What was the percent that the shirt was discounted? ______ %

Discount, Tax and Tip

Step-by-step guide:

- ✓ Discount = Multiply the regular price by the rate of discount
- ✓ Selling price = original price – discount
- ✓ Tax: To find tax, multiply the tax rate to the taxable amount (income, property value, etc.)
- ✓ To find tip, multiply the rate to the selling price.

Examples:

1) With an 20% discount, Ella was able to save $40 on a dress. What was the original price of the dress?
   $20\%\ of\ x = 40, \frac{20}{100} \times x = 40, x = \frac{100 \times 40}{20} = 200$

2) Sophia purchased a sofa for $250.40. The sofa is regularly priced at $313.125. What was the percent discount Sophia received on the sofa?
   Use this formula: $percent = Part \div base = 250.50 \div 313.125 = 0.80 = 80\%$
   Therefore, the discount is: $100\% - 80\% = 20\%$

Find the selling price of each item.

1) Original price of a computer: $200
   Tax: 10%, Selling price: $________
2) Original price of a laptop: $400
   Tax: 5%, Selling price: $________
3) Original price of a sofa: $500
   Tax: 8%, Selling price: $________
4) Original price of a car: $800
   Tax: 25%, Selling price: $________
5) Original price of a Table: $250
   Tax: 10%, Selling price: $________
6) Original price of a house: $1,500
   Tax: 15% Selling price: $________
7) Original price of a tablet: $600
   Discount: 20%, Selling price: $________
8) Original price of a chair: $450
   Discount: 25%, Selling price: $________
9) Original price of a book: $125
   Discount: 15%, Selling price: $________
10) Original price of a cellphone: $900
    Discount: 12%, Selling price: $________

Answers – Chapter 7

Percentage Calculations

1) 10
2) 20
3) 10
4) 21
5) 9
6) 40
7) 30
8) 9
9) 36
10) 24.94
11) 17.82
12) 79.52

Percent Problems

1) 10%
2) 80%
3) 200
4) 300
5) 40%
6) 20%
7) 31.25%
8) 20%
9) 250%
10) 425
11) 60
12) 320

Percent of Increase and Decrease

1) 25%
2) 50%
3) 20%
4) 20%
5) 16%
6) 10%
7) 20%

Markup, Discount, and Tip

1) $220.00
2) $420.00
3) $540.00
4) $1,000.00
5) $275.00
6) $1,725
7) $480.00
8) $337.50
9) $106.25
10) $792.00

Chapter 8:

Exponents and Variables

Math Topics that you'll learn in this chapter:

- ✓ Multiplication Property of Exponents
- ✓ Division Property of Exponents
- ✓ Powers of Products and Quotients
- ✓ Zero and Negative Exponents
- ✓ Negative Exponents and Negative Bases
- ✓ Scientific Notation
- ✓ Square Roots

Multiplication Property of Exponents

Step-by-step guide:

- ✓ Exponents are shorthand for repeated multiplication of the same number by itself. For example, instead of 2×2, we can write 2^2. For $3 \times 3 \times 3 \times 3$, we can write 3^4
- ✓ In algebra, a variable is a letter used to stand for a number. The most common letters are: $x, y, z, a, b, c, m, and\ n$.
- ✓ Exponent's rules: $x^a \times x^b = x^{a+b}$, $\frac{x^a}{x^b} = x^{a-b}$

  $(x^a)^b = x^{a \times b}$, $(xy)^a = x^a \times y^a$, $(\frac{a}{b})^c = \frac{a^c}{b^c}$

Examples:

1) Multiply. $4x^3 \times 2x^2 =$

   Use Exponent's rules: $x^a \times x^b = x^{a+b} \rightarrow x^3 \times x^2 = x^{3+2} = x^5$

   Then: $4x^3 \times 2x^2 = 8x^5$

2) Multiply. $(x^3 y^5)^2 =$

   Use Exponent's rules: $(x^a)^b = x^{a \times b}$. Then: $(x^3 y^5)^2 = x^{3\times 2} y^{5\times 2} = x^6 y^{10}$

Simplify and write the answer in exponential form.

1) $2x^2 \times 4x =$
2) $5x^4 \times x^2 =$
3) $8x^4 \times 3x^5 =$
4) $3x^2 \times 6xy =$
5) $2x^5 y \times 4x^2 y^3 =$
6) $9x^2 y^5 \times 5x^2 y^8 =$
7) $5x^2 y \times 5x^2 y^7 =$
8) $7x^6 \times 3x^9 y^4 =$
9) $8x^8 y^5 \times 7x^5 y^3 =$
10) $9x^6 x^2 \times 4xy^5 =$
11) $12xy^7 \times 2x^9 y^8 =$
12) $9x^9 y^{12} \times 9x^{14} y^{11} =$

Division Property of Exponents

Step-by-step guide:

✓ For division of exponents use these formulas: $\frac{x^a}{x^b} = x^{a-b}$, $x \neq 0$

$$\frac{x^a}{x^b} = \frac{1}{x^{b-a}}, x \neq 0, \qquad \frac{1}{x^b} = x^{-b}$$

Examples:

1) Simplify. $\frac{12x^2y}{4xy^3} =$

First cancel the common factor: $4 \rightarrow \frac{12x^2y}{4xy^3} = \frac{3x^2y}{xy^3}$

Use Exponent's rules: $\frac{x^a}{x^b} = x^{a-b} \rightarrow \frac{x^2}{x} = x^{2-1} = x$ and $\frac{y}{y^3} = y^{1-3} = y^{-2}$

Then: $\frac{12x^2y}{4xy^3} = \frac{3x}{y^2}$

2) Divide. $\frac{18x^{-6}}{2x^{-3}} =$

Use Exponent's rules: $\frac{x^a}{x^b} = \frac{1}{x^{b-a}} \rightarrow \frac{x^{-6}}{x^{-3}} = \frac{1}{x^{-3-(-6)}} = \frac{1}{x^{-3+6}} = \frac{1}{x^3}$

Then: $\frac{18x^{-6}}{2x^{-3}} = \frac{9}{x^3}$

Simplify.

1) $\frac{5^2 \times 5^3}{5^4 \times 5^2} =$

2) $\frac{4x}{8x^2} =$

3) $\frac{15x^6}{3x^5} =$

4) $\frac{18x^5}{12x^8} =$

5) $\frac{24x^5}{4y^3} =$

6) $\frac{36xy^3}{2x^5y^2} =$

7) $\frac{8x^8y}{3xy^2} =$

8) $\frac{20x^5y^9}{4x^3} =$

9) $\frac{28x^2}{8x^5y^3} =$

10) $\frac{25yx^4}{5yx^8} =$

11) $\frac{45x^4y}{9x^8y^2} =$

12) $\frac{4x^8y^2}{20x^8y} =$

Powers of Products and Quotients

Step-by-step guide:

- ✓ For any nonzero numbers a and b and any integer x, $(ab)^x = a^x \times b^x$.

Example:

1) Simplify. $(6x^2y^4)^2 =$

   Use Exponent's rules: $(x^a)^b = x^{a \times b}$

   $(6x^2y^4)^2 = (6)^2(x^2)^2(y^4)^2 = 36x^{2\times2}y^{4\times2} = 36x^4y^8$

2) Simplify. $(\frac{5x}{2x^2})^2 =$

   First cancel the common factor: $x \rightarrow \left(\frac{5x}{2x^2}\right)^2 = \left(\frac{5}{2x}\right)^2$

   Use Exponent's rules: $(\frac{a}{b})^c = \frac{a^c}{b^c}$

   Then: $(\frac{5}{2x})^2 = \frac{5^2}{(2x)^2} = \frac{25}{4x^2}$

Simplify.

1) $(x^2y^6)^2 =$
2) $(x^3 \times y)^2 =$
3) $(2x^5y^3)^2 =$
4) $(3x^3y^6)^2 =$
5) $(4x^5y^6)^3 =$
6) $(5x \times 2y^5)^2 =$
7) $(\frac{3x}{x^2})^3 =$
8) $\left(\frac{x^2y^3}{x^2y^2}\right)^3 =$
9) $\left(\frac{16x}{4x^6}\right)^2 =$
10) $\left(\frac{2x^5}{x^2y^2}\right)^2 =$
11) $\left(\frac{xy^2}{x^2y^3}\right)^{-2} =$
12) $\left(\frac{8xy^2}{x^3}\right)^2 =$

Zero and Negative Exponents

Step-by-step guide:

✓ A negative exponent simply means that the base is on the wrong side of the fraction line, so you need to flip the base to the other side. For instance, "x^{-2}" (pronounced as "ecks to the minus two") just means "x^2" but underneath, as in $\frac{1}{x^2}$.

Example:

1) Evaluate. $(\frac{2}{3})^{-2} =$

Use Exponent's rules: $\frac{1}{x^b} = x^{-b} \rightarrow (\frac{2}{3})^{-2} = \frac{1}{(\frac{2}{3})^2} = \frac{1}{\frac{2^2}{3^2}}$

Now use fraction rule: $\frac{1}{\frac{b}{c}} = \frac{c}{b} \rightarrow \frac{1}{\frac{2^2}{3^2}} = \frac{3^2}{2^2} = \frac{9}{4}$

2) Evaluate. $(\frac{4}{5})^{-3} =$

Use Exponent's rules: $\frac{1}{x^b} = x^{-b} \rightarrow (\frac{4}{5})^{-3} = \frac{1}{(\frac{4}{5})^3} = \frac{1}{\frac{4^3}{5^3}}$

Now use fraction rule: $\frac{1}{\frac{b}{c}} = \frac{c}{b} \rightarrow \frac{1}{\frac{4^3}{5^3}} = \frac{5^3}{4^3} = \frac{125}{64}$

Evaluate the following expressions.

1) $3^{-2} =$

2) $2^{-3} =$

3) $5^{-3} =$

4) $4^{-3} =$

5) $6^{-3} =$

6) $8^{-2} =$

7) $5^{-4} =$

8) $10^{-2} =$

9) $(\frac{1}{5})^{-1}$

10) $(\frac{1}{4})^{-2} =$

11) $(\frac{1}{5})^{-3} =$

12) $(\frac{3}{4})^{-2} =$

Negative Exponents and Negative Bases

Step-by-step guide:

- ✓ Make the power positive. A negative exponent is the reciprocal of that number with a positive exponent.
- ✓ The parenthesis is important!
- ✓ 5^{-2} is not the same as $(-5)^{-2}$

$$(-5)^{-2} = -\frac{1}{5^2} \text{ and } (-5)^{-2} = +\frac{1}{5^2}$$

Example:

1) Simplify. $(\frac{5a}{6c})^{-2} =$

Use Exponent's rules: $\frac{1}{x^b} = x^{-b} \rightarrow (\frac{5a}{6c})^{-2} = \frac{1}{(\frac{5a}{6c})^2} = \frac{1}{\frac{5^2a^2}{6^2c^2}}$

Now use fraction rule: $\frac{1}{\frac{b}{c}} = \frac{c}{b} \rightarrow \frac{1}{\frac{5^2a^2}{6^2c^2}} = \frac{6^2c^2}{5^2a^2}$

Then: $\frac{6^2c^2}{5^2a^2} = \frac{36c^2}{25a^2}$

2) Simplify. $(\frac{2x}{3yz})^{-3} =$

Use Exponent's rules: $\frac{1}{x^b} = x^{-b} \rightarrow (\frac{2x}{3yz})^{-3} = \frac{1}{(\frac{2x}{3yz})^3} = \frac{1}{\frac{2^3x^3}{3^3y^3z^3}}$

Now use fraction rule: $\frac{1}{\frac{b}{c}} = \frac{c}{b} \rightarrow \frac{1}{\frac{2^3x^3}{3^3y^3z^3}} = \frac{3^3y^3z^3}{2^3x^3} = \frac{27y^3z^3}{8x^3}$

Simplify.

1) $2x^{-2}y^{-3} =$

2) $3x^{-5}y^{-2} =$

3) $6a^{-3}b^{-5} =$

4) $7x^4y^{-3} =$

5) $-\frac{9}{x^{-4}} =$

6) $\frac{12b}{-9c^{-5}} =$

7) $\frac{16ab}{a^{-2}b^{-3}} =$

8) $\frac{15n^{-2}}{20p^{-3}} =$

9) $\frac{16ab^{-5}}{4c^{-2}} =$

10) $(\frac{5x}{2y})^{-2} =$

11) $(-\frac{2x}{3yz})^{-4} =$

12) $\frac{5ab^{-3}}{-3c^{-2}} =$

13) $(-\frac{x^5}{x^3})^{-2} =$

Scientific Notation

Step-by-step guide:

- ✓ It is used to write very big or very small numbers in decimal form.
- ✓ In scientific notation all numbers are written in the form of:

$$m \times 10^n$$

Decimal notation	Scientific notation
5	5×10^0
$-25{,}000$	-2.5×10^4
0.5	5×10^{-1}
$2{,}122.456$	$2{,}122456 \times 10^{-3}$

Example:

1) Write $\mathbf{0.00015}$ in scientific notation.

First, move the decimal point to the right so that you have a number that is between 1 and 10. Then: $N = 1.5$

Second, determine how many places the decimal moved in step 1 by the power of 10.

Then: 10^{-4} → When the decimal moved to the right, the exponent is negative.

Then: $0.00015 = 1.5 \times 10^{-4}$

2) Write $\mathbf{9.5 \times 10^{-5}}$ in standard notation.

10^{-5} → When the decimal moved to the right, the exponent is negative.

Then: $9.5 \times 10^{-5} = 0.000095$

Write each number in scientific notation.

1) $15{,}000{,}000 =$

2) $67{,}000 =$

3) $0.000819 =$

4) $0.00092 =$

Write each number in standard notation.

5) $4.5 \times 10^3 =$

6) $8 \times 10^{-4} =$

7) $6 \times 10^{-1} =$

8) $9 \times 10^{-2} =$

Square Roots

Step-by-step guide:

✓ A square root of x is a number r whose square is: $r^2 = x$

r is a square root of x.

Example:

1) Find the square root of $\sqrt{169}$.

First factor the number: $169 = 13^2$, Then: $\sqrt{169} = \sqrt{13^2}$

Now use radical rule: $\sqrt[n]{a^n} = a$

Then: $\sqrt{13^2} = 13$

2) Evaluate. $\sqrt{9} \times \sqrt{25} =$

First factor the numbers: $9 = 3^2$ and $25 = 5^2$

Then: $\sqrt{9} \times \sqrt{25} = \sqrt{3^2} \times \sqrt{5^2}$

Now use radical rule: $\sqrt[n]{a^n} = a$, Then: $\sqrt{3^2} \times \sqrt{5^2} = 3 \times 5 = 15$

Evaluate.

1) $\sqrt{16} \times \sqrt{4} =$ ________

2) $\sqrt{9} \times \sqrt{49} =$ ________

3) $\sqrt{4} \times \sqrt{8} =$ ________

4) $\sqrt{9} \times \sqrt{6} =$ ________

5) $\sqrt{25} \times \sqrt{5} =$ ________

6) $\sqrt{6} \times \sqrt{6} =$ ________

7) $\sqrt{5} + \sqrt{5} =$ ________

8) $\sqrt{12} + \sqrt{12} =$ ________

9) $3\sqrt{6} - 2\sqrt{6} =$ ________

10) $3\sqrt{5} \times 2\sqrt{5} =$ ________

11) $6\sqrt{8} \times 2\sqrt{8} =$ ________

12) $6\sqrt{4} - \sqrt{16} =$ ________

Answers – Chapter 8

Multiplication Property of Exponents

1) $8x^3$
2) $5x^6$
3) $24x^9$
4) $18x^3y$
5) $8x^7y^4$
6) $45x^4y^{13}$
7) $25x^4y^8$
8) $21x^{15}y^4$
9) $56x^{13}y^8$
10) $36x^9y^5$
11) $24x^{10}y^{15}$
12) $81x^{23}y^{23}$

Division Property of Exponents

1) $\frac{1}{5}$
2) $\frac{1}{2x}$
3) $5x$
4) $\frac{3}{2x^3}$
5) $\frac{6x^5}{y^3}$
6) $\frac{18y}{x^4}$
7) $\frac{8x^7}{3y}$
8) $5x^2y^9$
9) $\frac{7}{2x^3y^3}$
10) $\frac{5}{x^4}$
11) $\frac{5}{x^4y}$
12) $\frac{y}{5}$

Powers of Products and Quotients

1) x^4y^{12}
2) x^6y^2
3) $4x^{10}y^6$
4) $9x^6y^{12}$
5) $64x^{15}y^{18}$
6) $100x^2y^{10}$
7) $\frac{27}{x^3}$
8) y^3
9) $\frac{16}{x^{10}}$
10) $\frac{4x^6}{y^4}$
11) x^2y^2
12) $\frac{64y^{10}}{x^4}$

Zero and Negative Exponents

1) $\frac{1}{9}$
2) $\frac{1}{8}$
3) $\frac{1}{125}$
4) $\frac{1}{64}$
5) $\frac{1}{216}$
6) $\frac{1}{64}$
7) $\frac{1}{625}$
8) $\frac{1}{100}$
9) 5
10) 16
11) 125
12) $\frac{16}{9}$

Negative Exponents and Negative Bases

1) $\frac{2}{x^2 y^3}$
2) $\frac{3}{x^5 y^2}$
3) $\frac{6}{a^3 b^5}$
4) $\frac{7x^4}{y^3}$
5) $-9x^4$
6) $-\frac{4bc^5}{3}$
7) $16a^3b^4$
8) $\frac{3p^3}{4n^2}$
9) $\frac{4ac^2}{b^5}$
10) $\frac{4y^2}{25x^2}$
11) $\frac{81y^4z^4}{16x^4}$
12) $-\frac{5ac^2}{3b^3}$
13) $\frac{1}{x^4}$

Scientific Notation

1) 1.5×10^7
2) 6.7×10^4
3) 8.19×10^{-4}
4) 9.2×10^{-4}
5) 4,500
6) 0.0008
7) 0.6
8) 0.09

Square Roots

1) 8
2) 21
3) $4\sqrt{2}$
4) $3\sqrt{6}$
5) $5\sqrt{5}$
6) 6
7) $2\sqrt{5}$
8) $4\sqrt{3}$
9) $\sqrt{6}$
10) 30
11) 96
12) 8

Chapter 9: Expressions and Variables

Math Topics that you'll learn in this chapter:

- ✓ Simplifying Variable Expressions
- ✓ Simplifying Polynomial Expressions
- ✓ Translate Phrases into an Algebraic Statement
- ✓ The Distributive Property
- ✓ Evaluating One Variable
- ✓ Evaluating Two Variables
- ✓ Combining like Terms

Simplifying Variable Expressions

Step-by-step guide:

- ✓ In algebra, a variable is a letter used to stand for a number. The most common letters are: $x, y, z, a, b, c, m, and\ n$.
- ✓ algebraic expression is an expression contains integers, variables, and the math operations such as addition, subtraction, multiplication, division, etc.
- ✓ In an expression, we can combine "like" terms. (values with same variable and same power)

Examples:

1) Simplify this expression. $(2x + 3x + 4) = ?$
   Combine like terms. Then: $(2x + 3x + 4) = 5x + 4$ (remember you cannot combine variables and numbers.
2) Simplify this expression. $12 - 3x^2 + 5x + 4x^2 = ?$
   Combine "like" terms: $-3x^2 + 4x^2 = x^2$
   Then: $= 12 + x^2 + 5x$. Write in standard form (biggest powers first): $x^2 + 5x + 12$

 ***Simplify each expression.***

1) $x - 4 + 6 - 2x =$
2) $3 - 4x + 14 - 3x =$
3) $33x - 5 + 13 + 4x =$
4) $-3 - x^2 - 7x^2 =$
5) $4 + 11x^2 + 3 =$
6) $7x^2 + 5x + 6x^2 =$
7) $42x + 15 + 3x^2 =$
8) $6x(x - 2) - 5 =$
9) $7x - 6 + 9x + 3x^2 =$
10) $(-5)(7x - 2) + 12x =$
11) $15x - 6(6 - 7x) =$
12) $25x + 6(7x + 2) + 14 =$

Simplifying Polynomial Expressions

Step-by-step guide:

✓ In mathematics, a polynomial is an expression consisting of variables and coefficients that involves only the operations of addition, subtraction, multiplication, and non-negative integer exponents of variables.

$$P(x) = a_n x^n + a_{n-1} x^{n-1} + \ldots + a_2 x^2 + a_1 x + a_0$$

Examples:

1) Simplify this Polynomial Expressions. $x^2 - 5x^3 + 2x^4 - 4x^3 =$
   Combine "like" terms: $-5x^3 - 4x^3 = -9x^3$
   Then: $x^2 - 5x^3 + 2x^4 - 4x^3 = x^2 - 9x^3 + 2x^4$
   Then write in standard form: $= 2x^4 - 9x^3 + x^2$

2) Simplify this expression. $(2x^2 - x^3) - (x^3 - 4x^2) =$
   First use distributive property: → multiply $(-)$ into $(x^3 - 4x^2)$
   $(2x^2 - x^3) - (x^3 - 4x^2) = 2x^2 - x^3 - x^3 + 4x^2$
   Then combine "like" terms: $2x^2 - x^3 - x^3 + 4x^2 = 6x^2 - 2x^3$
   And write in standard form: $= -2x^3 + 6x^2$

Simplify each polynomial.

1) $4x^2 + 7x^3 - 9x^2 + 15x =$ ______________________

2) $3x^4 - 6x^5 + 7x^4 - 9x^2 =$ ______________________

3) $6x^3 + 18x - x^2 - 3x^3 =$ ______________________

4) $3x^3 - (5x^4 + 3x) + x^2 =$ ______________________

5) $x^4 - 3(x^2 + x) + 2x =$ ______________________

6) $(6x^3 - 4) + 3(4x^2 - 2x^3) =$ ______________________

7) $(5x^3 - 3x) - 3(6x^3 - 4x^4) =$ ______________________

8) $3(6x - 2x^3) - 4(2x^3 + 3x^2) =$ ______________________

Translate Phrases into an Algebraic Statement

Step-by-step guide:

Translating key words and phrases into algebraic expressions:

- ✓ Addition: plus, more than, the sum of, etc.
- ✓ Subtraction: minus, less than, decreased, etc.
- ✓ Multiplication: times, product, multiplied, etc.
- ✓ Division: quotient, divided, ratio, etc.

Examples:

Write an algebraic expression for each phrase.

1) 12 times the sum of 5 and x.
   Sum of 5 and x: $5 + x$. Times means multiplication. Then: $12 \times (5 + x)$

2) Nine more than a number is 18.
   More than mean plus a number $= x$
   Then: $9 + x = 18$

Write an algebraic expression for each phrase.

1) 9 decreased by y. ________________
2) Add y to 16. ________________
3) The square of 8. ________________
4) 7 multiplied by x. ________________
5) Subtract 22 from y. ________________
6) 13 divided by x. ________________
7) x raised to the fifth power. ________________
8) The sum of five and a number. ________________
9) The difference between fifty–four and y. ________________
10) The quotient of eleven and a number. ________________
11) The quotient of the square of b and 8. ________________
12) The difference between x and 24 is 18. ________________

The Distributive Property

Step-by-step guide:

- ✓ Distributive Property:

$$a(b+c) = ab + ac$$

Examples:

1) Simply. $(-2)(x-3) =$

Use Distributive Property formula: $a(b+c) = ab + ac$
$(-2)(x-3) = -2x + 6$

2) Simply$(5)(6x-3) =$

Use Distributive Property formula: $a(b+c) = ab + ac$
$(5)(6x-3) = 30x - 15$

✍ ***Use the distributive property to simply each expression.***

1) $(-4)(x-7) =$
2) $-(8-5x) =$
3) $7(7+3x) =$
4) $3(14+3x) =$
5) $(-7x+6)3 =$
6) $6(5+7x) =$
7) $12(4x+3) =$
8) $(-3x+5)5 =$
9) $(5-8x)(-9) =$
10) $(-4)(2-16x) =$
11) $12(4x-15) =$
12) $(-15x+20)(-2) =$

Evaluating One Variable

Step-by-step guide:

- ✓ To evaluate one variable expression, find the variable and substitute a number for that variable.
- ✓ Perform the arithmetic operations.

Examples:

1) Solve this expression. $18 - 2x, x = 2$

First substitute 2 for x, then:

$18 - 2x = 18 - 2(2) = 18 - 4 = 14$

2) Solve this expression. $5 - 2x, x = -1$

First substitute -1 for x, then:

$5 - 2x = 5 - 2(-1) = 5 + 2 = 7$

Evaluate each expression using the value given.

1) $3x - 6, x = 3$
2) $6x + 5, x = -2$
3) $10 - x, x = 2$
4) $x + 3, x = 4$
5) $2x + 6, x = 7$
6) $12 - 2x, x = -3$
7) $4x + 5, x = 3$
8) $5x + 7, x = -2$
9) $12 + 3x - 7, x = 2$
10) $6(5x + 3), x = 7$
11) $3(-6x - 3), x = 4$
12) $8x - 4x + 14, x = 5$

Evaluating Two Variables

Step-by-step guide:

✓ To evaluate an algebraic expression, substitute a number for each variable and perform the arithmetic operations.

Examples:

1) Solve this expression. $4(2a-b), a=2, b=-1$

First substitute 2 for a, and -1 for b, then:

$4(2a-b), 8a-4b = 8(2)-4(-1) = 16+4 = 20$

2) Solve this expression. $2x+6y, x=1, y=2$

First substitute 1 for x, and 2 for y, then:

$2x+6y = 2(1)+6(2) = 2+12 = 14$

Evaluate each expression using the values given.

1) $x+2y$,
$x=1, y=2$

2) $2x-3y$,
$x=1, y=-2$

3) $-a+5b$,
$a=-2, b=3$

4) $-3a+5b$,
$a=5, b=2$

5) $5x+8-3y$,
$x=5, y=4$

6) $3x+5y$,
$x=2, y=3$

7) $7x+6y$,
$x=2, y=4$

8) $3a-(12-b)$,
$a=3, b=5$

9) $4z+20+7k$,
$z=-4, k=5$

10) $xy+15+4x$,
$x=6, y=3$

11) $8x+3-5y+4$,
$x=6, y=3$

12) $5+2(-3x-4y)$,
$x=6, y=5$

Combining like Terms

Step-by-step guide:

- ✓ Terms are separated by "+" and "-" signs.
- ✓ Like terms are terms with same variables and same powers.
- ✓ Be sure to use the "+" or "-" that is in front of the coefficient.

Examples:

1) Simplify this expression. $(-2)(2x-2)=$

First use Distributive Property formula: $a(b+c)=ab+ac$
$(-2)(2x-2)=-4x+4$

2) Simplify this expression. $4(-2x+6)=$

Use Distributive Property formula: $a(b+c)=a+ac$
$4(-2x+6)=-8x+24$

Simplify each expression.

1) $-4x+x+5=$

2) $-2(3x-4)=$

3) $-14x+6-12x=$

4) $8x-12-3x+3=$

5) $13x+5x-22=$

6) $3(4x+8)+7x=$

7) $3(5-2x)-20x=$

8) $-5x-(7-15x)=$

9) $5(-15x+3)-17x=$

10) $-8x-23+19x=$

11) $24x-13x+8-6x=$

12) $(-3)(8x-5)-19x=$

Answers – Chapter 9

Simplifying Variable Expressions

1) $-x+2$
2) $-7x+17$
3) $37x+8$
4) $-8x^2-3$
5) $11x^2+7$
6) $13x^2+5x$
7) $3x^2+42x+15$
8) $6x^2-12x-5$
9) $3x^2+16x-6$
10) $-23x+10$
11) $57x-36$
12) $67x+26$

Simplifying Polynomial Expressions

1) $7x^3-5x^2+15x$
2) $-6x^5+10x^4-9x^2$
3) $3x^3-x^2+18x$
4) $-5x^4+3x^3+x^2-3x$
5) x^4-3x^2-x
6) $12x^2-4$
7) $12x^4-13x^3-3x$
8) $-14x^3-12x^2+18x$

Translate Phrases into an Algebraic Statement

1) $9-y$
2) $y+16$
3) 8^2
4) $7x$
5) $y-22$
6) $\frac{13}{x}$
7) x^5
8) $5+x$
9) $54-y$
10) $\frac{11}{x}$
11) $\frac{b^2}{8}$
12) $x-24=18$

The Distributive Property

1) $-4x+28$
2) $5x-8$
3) $21x+49$
4) $9x+42$
5) $-21x+18$
6) $42x+30$
7) $48x+36$
8) $-15x+25$
9) $72x-45$
10) $64x-8$
11) $48x-180$
12) $30x-40$

Evaluating One Variable

1) 3
2) -7
3) 8
4) 7
5) 20
6) 18
7) 17
8) -3
9) 11
10) 228

11) -81

12) 34

Evaluating Two Variables

1) 5
2) 8
3) 17
4) -5
5) 21
6) 21
7) 38
8) 2
9) 39
10) 57
11) 40
12) -71

Combining like Terms

1) $-3x+5$
2) $-6x+8$
3) $-26x+6$
4) $5x-9$
5) $18x-22$
6) $19x+24$
7) $-26x+15$
8) $10x-7$
9) $-92x+15$
10) $11x-23$
11) $5x+8$
12) $-43x+15$

Chapter 10: Equations and Inequalities

Math Topics that you'll learn in this chapter:

- ✓ One–Step Equations
- ✓ Multi–Step Equations
- ✓ Graphing Single–Variable Inequalities
- ✓ One–Step Inequalities
- ✓ Multi–Step Inequalities

"Life is a math equation. In order to gain the most, you have to know how to convert negatives into positives."

~ Anonymous

One–Step Equations

Step-by-step guide:

- ✓ The values of two expressions on both sides of an equation are equal. $ax + b = c$
- ✓ You only need to perform one Math operation in order to solve the one-step equations.
- ✓ To solve one-step equation, find the inverse (opposite) operation is being performed.
- ✓ The inverse operations are:
  - Addition and subtraction
  - Multiplication and division

Examples:

1) Solve this equation. $2x = 16, x = ?$
   Here, the operation is multiplication (variable x is multiplied by 3) and its inverse operation is division. To solve this equation, divide both sides of equation by 2:
   $$2x = 16 \rightarrow 2x \div 2 = 16 \div 2 \rightarrow x = 8$$

2) Solve this equation. $x + 12 = 0, x = ?$
   Here, the operation is addition and its inverse operation is subtraction. To solve this equation, subtract 12 from both sides of the equation: $x + 12 - 12 = 0 - 12$
   Then simplify: $x + 12 - 12 = 0 - 12 \rightarrow x = -12$

Solve each equation.

1) $14 = -2 + x, x =$ ____
2) $x + 7 = 14, x =$ ____
3) $x - 3 = 15, x =$ ____
4) $6 = 14 + x, x =$ ____
5) $x - 4 = 5, x =$ ____
6) $3 - x = -11, x =$ ____
7) $x - 5 = -15, x =$ ____
8) $x - 14 = 14, x =$ ____
9) $x - 15 = -30, x =$ ____
10) $x - 12 = 34, x =$ ____
11) $9 - x = 5, x =$ ____
12) $x - 16 = 16, x =$ ____

Multi–Step Equations

Step-by-step guide:

- ✓ Combine "like" terms on one side.
- ✓ Bring variables to one side by adding or subtracting.
- ✓ Simplify using the inverse of addition or subtraction.
- ✓ Simplify further by using the inverse of multiplication or division.

Examples:

1) Solve this equation. $-(8-x)=6$

First use Distributive Property: $-(8-x)=-8+x$

Now solve by subtract 6 to both sides of the equation. $-8+x=6 \rightarrow -8+x-6=6-6$

Now simplify: $-14+x=0 \rightarrow x=14$

2) Solve this equation. $2x+5=15-x$

First bring variables to one side by adding x to both sides.

$2x+5=15-x \rightarrow 3x+5=15$. Now, subtract 15 from both sides:

$3x+5-15=15-15 \rightarrow 3x-10=0 \rightarrow 3x=10$

Now, divide both sides by 3: $3x=10 \rightarrow 3x \div 3=\frac{10}{3} \rightarrow x=\frac{10}{3}$

Solve each equation.

1) $-(3-x)=7$
2) $3x-15=12$
3) $3x-3=9$
4) $3x-15=6$
5) $-3(5+x)=3$
6) $-5(3+x)=5$
7) $24=-(x-7)$
8) $6(4-2x)=30$
9) $18-4x=-9-x$
10) $14-2x=14+x$
11) $30+15x=-6+3x$
12) $18=(-4x)-9+3$

Graphing Single–Variable Inequalities

Step-by-step guide:

- ✓ Inequality is similar to equations and uses symbols for "less than" (<) and "greater than" (>).
- ✓ To solve inequalities, we need to isolate the variable. (like in equations)
- ✓ To graph an inequality, find the value of the inequality on the number line.
- ✓ For less than or greater than draw open circle on the value of the variable.
- ✓ If there is an equal sign too, then use filled circle.
- ✓ Draw a line to the right or to the left for greater or less than.

Examples:

1) Draw a graph for $x > 4$

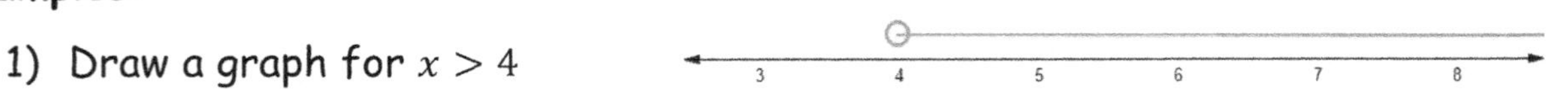

Since, the variable is greater than 4, then we need to find 4 and draw an open circle above it. Then, draw a line to the right.

2) Graph this inequality. $x < 5$

Draw a graph for each inequality.

1) $x > 2$

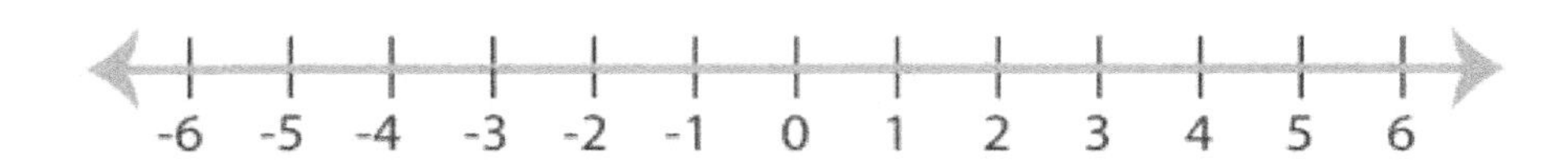

2) $x < -2$

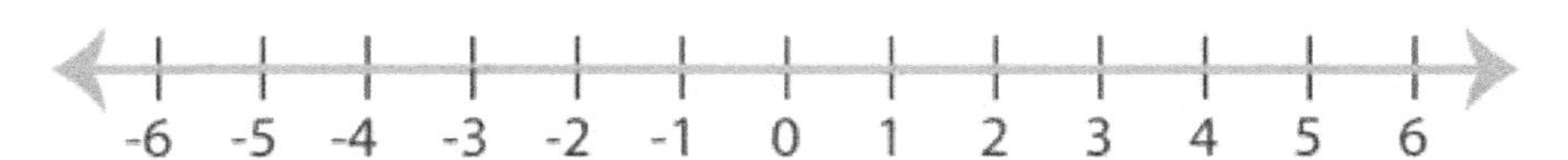

3) $x < 4$

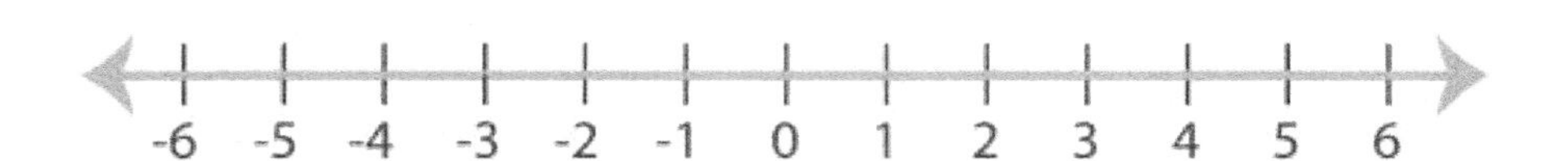

4) $x > -1$

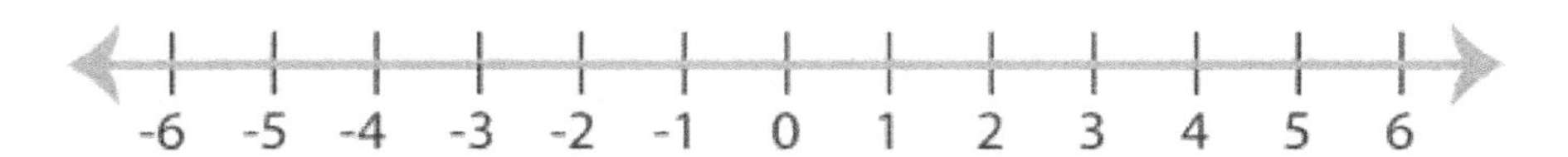

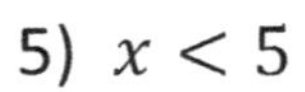

5) $x < 5$

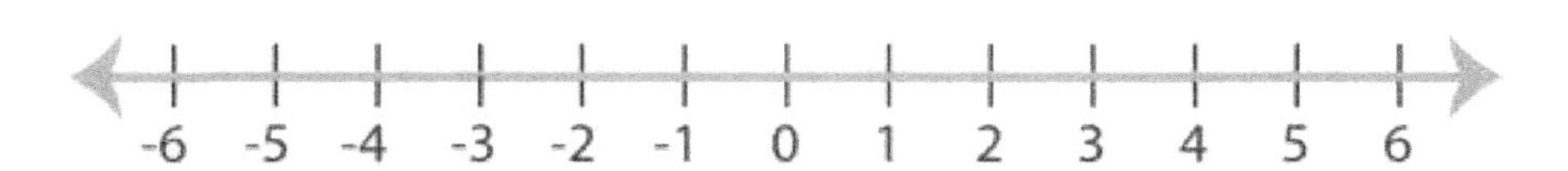

One–Step Inequalities

Step-by-step guide:

- ✓ Similar to equations, first isolate the variable by using inverse operation.
- ✓ For dividing or multiplying both sides by negative numbers, flip the direction of the inequality sign.

Examples:

1) Solve and graph the inequality. $x + 2 \geq 3$.

Subtract 2 from both sides. $x + 2 \geq 3 \rightarrow x + 2 - 2 \geq 3 - 2$, then: $x \geq 1$

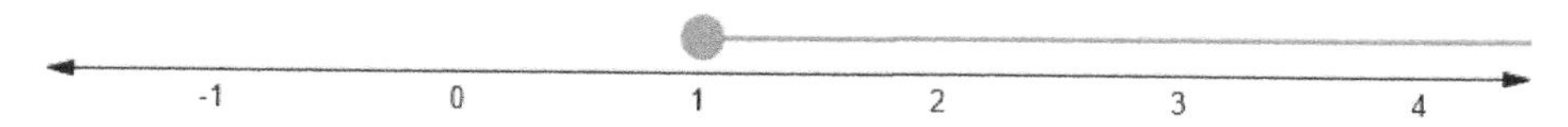

2) Solve this inequality. $x - 1 \leq 2$

Add 1 to both sides. $x - 1 \leq 2 \rightarrow x - 1 + 1 \leq 2 + 1$, then: $x \leq 3$

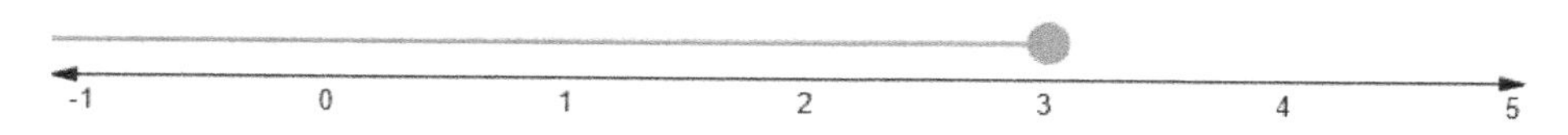

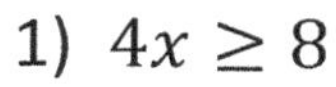 ***Solve each inequality and graph it.***

1) $4x \geq 8$

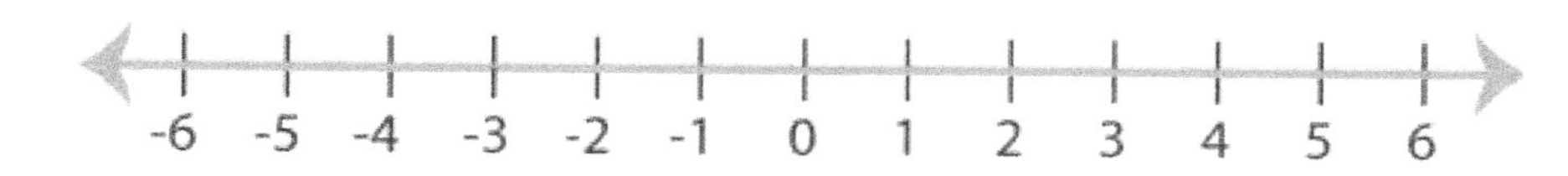

2) $2 + x \leq 6$

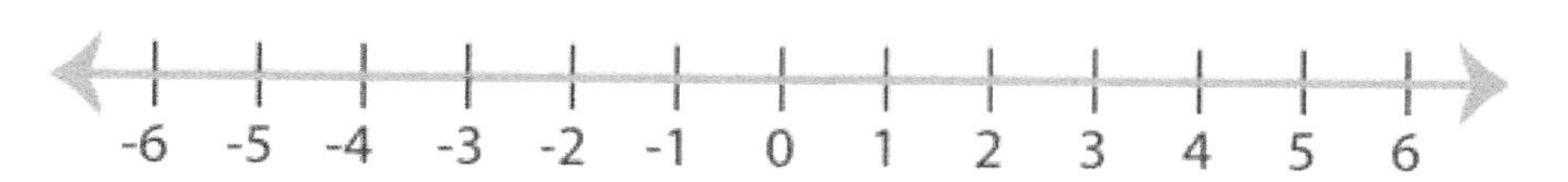

3) $x + 4 \leq 9$

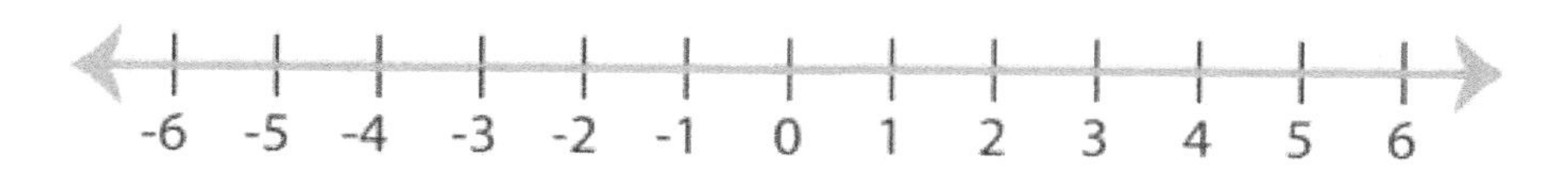

4) $8x \geq 24$

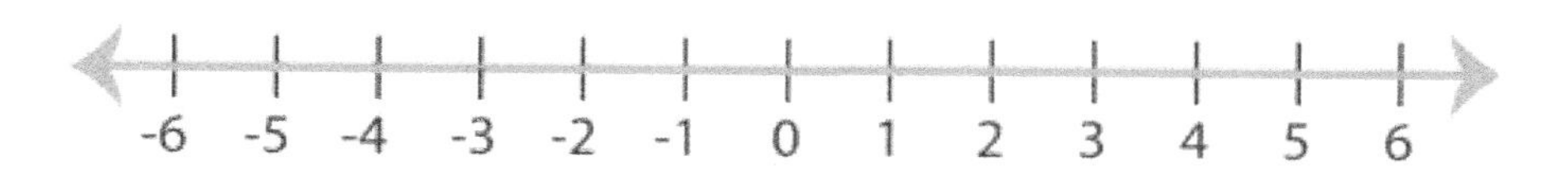

5) $5x \leq 20$

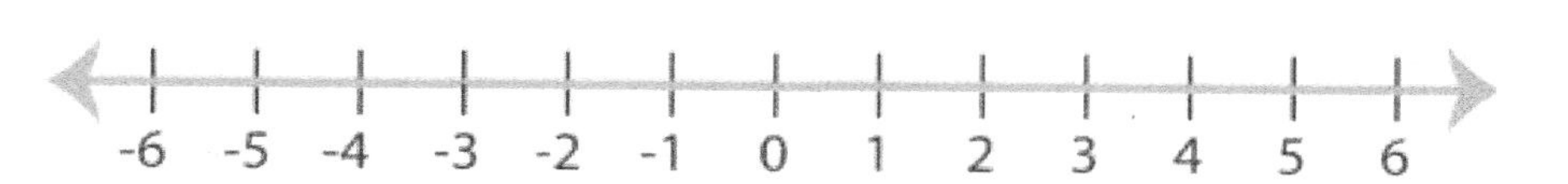

Multi–Step Inequalities

Step-by-step guide:

- ✓ Isolate the variable.
- ✓ Simplify using the inverse of addition or subtraction.
- ✓ Simplify further by using the inverse of multiplication or division.

Examples:

1) Solve this inequality. $x - 2 \leq 4$

   First add 2 to both sides: $x - 2 + 2 \leq 4 + 2 \rightarrow x \leq 6$

2) Solve this inequality. $2x + 6 \leq 10$

   First add 4 to both sides: $2x + 6 - 6 \leq 10 - 6$

   Then simplify: $2x + 6 - 6 \leq 10 - 6 \rightarrow 2x \leq 4$

   Now divide both sides by 2: $\frac{2x}{2} \leq \frac{4}{2} \rightarrow x \leq 2$

Solve each inequality.

1) $x - 5 \leq 4$
2) $2x - 2 \leq 12$
3) $3 + 2x \leq 11$
4) $x - 6 \geq 12$
5) $3x - 6 \leq 12$
6) $7x - 3 \leq 18$
7) $2x - 3 < 23$
8) $15 - 2x \geq -15$
9) $7 + 3x < 25$
10) $2 + 4x \geq 18$
11) $7 + 3x < 34$
12) $5x - 2 < 8$

Answers – Chapter 10

One–Step Equations

1) 16
2) 7
3) 18
4) -8
5) 9
6) 14
7) -10
8) 28
9) -15
10) 46
11) 4
12) 32

Multi–Step Equations

1) 10
2) 9
3) 4
4) 7
5) -6
6) -4
7) -17
8) $-\frac{1}{2}$
9) 9
10) 0
11) -3
12) -6

Graphing Single–Variable Inequalities

1)

2)

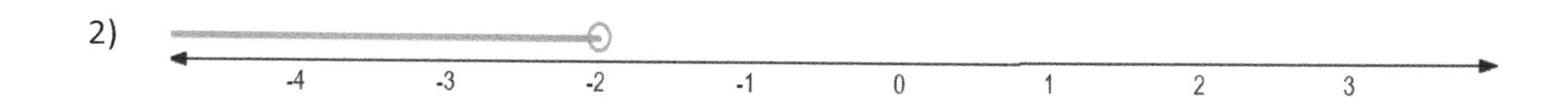

3)

4)

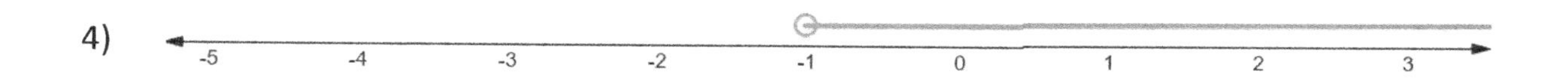

5)

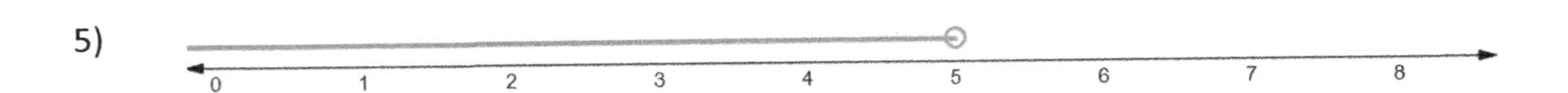

One–Step Inequalities

1)

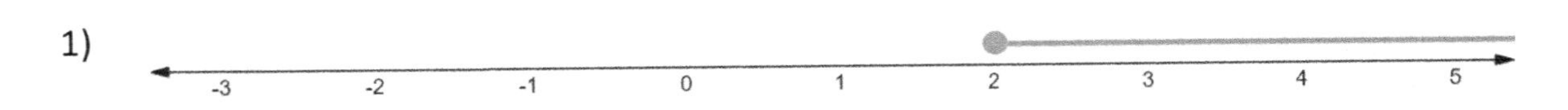

2)

3)

4)

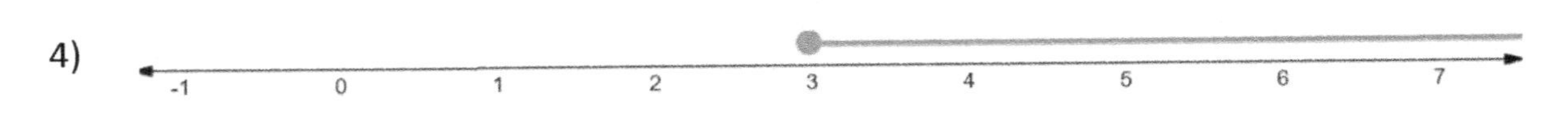

5)

Multi–Step inequalities

1) $x \leq 9$
2) $x \leq 7$
3) $x \leq 4$
4) $x \geq 18$
5) $x \leq 6$
6) $x \leq 3$
7) $x < 13$
8) $x \leq 15$
9) $x < 6$
10) $x \geq 4$
11) $x < 9$
12) $x < 2$

Chapter 11: Geometry and Solid Figures

Math Topics that you'll learn in this chapter:

- ✓ The Pythagorean Theorem
- ✓ Triangles
- ✓ Polygons
- ✓ Circles
- ✓ Trapezoids
- ✓ Cubes
- ✓ Rectangle Prisms
- ✓ Cylinder

The Pythagorean Theorem

Step-by-step guide:

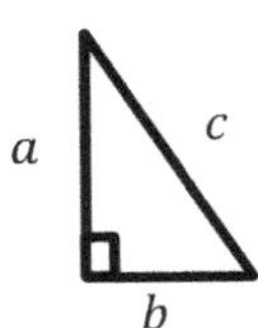

- ✓ In any right triangle: $a^2 + b^2 = c^2$

Example:

1) Right triangle ABC has two legs of lengths 9 cm (AB) and 12 cm (AC). What is the length of the third side (BC)?

   Use Pythagorean Theorem: $a^2 + b^2 = c^2$

   Then: $a^2 + b^2 = c^2 \rightarrow 9^2 + 12^2 = c^2 \rightarrow 81 + 144 = c^2$

   $c^2 = 225 \rightarrow c = 15\ cm$

2) Find the missing length.

   Use Pythagorean Theorem: $a^2 + b^2 = c^2$

   Then: $a^2 + b^2 = c^2 \rightarrow 8^2 + 6^2 = c^2 \rightarrow 64 + 36 = c^2$

   $c^2 = 100 \rightarrow c = 10$

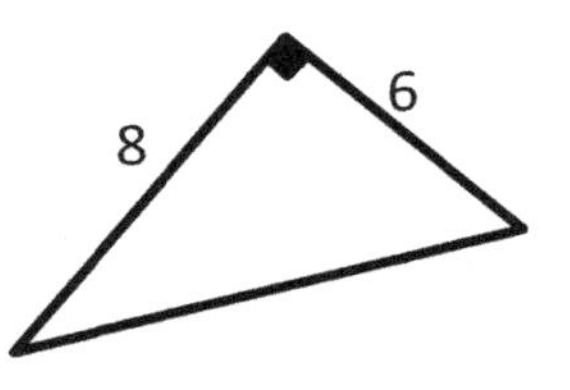

Find the missing side?

1)
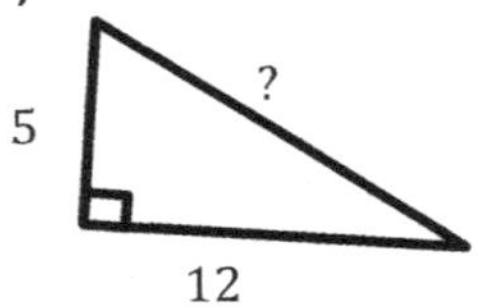

2)
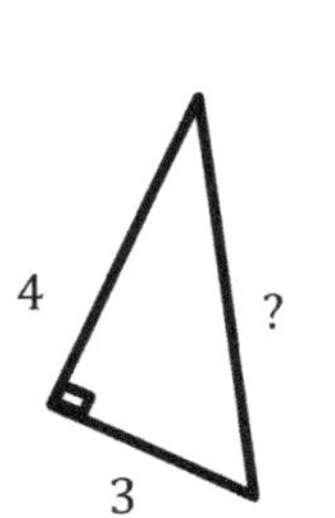

3)
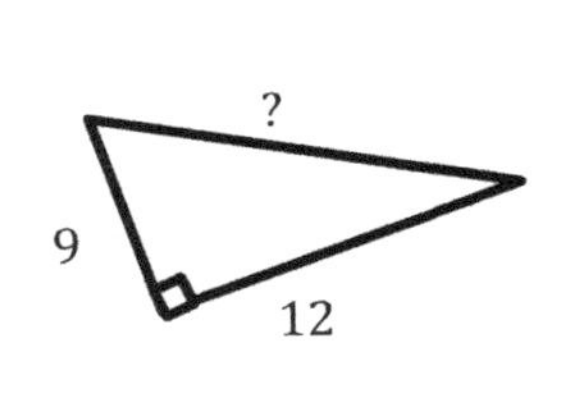

4)
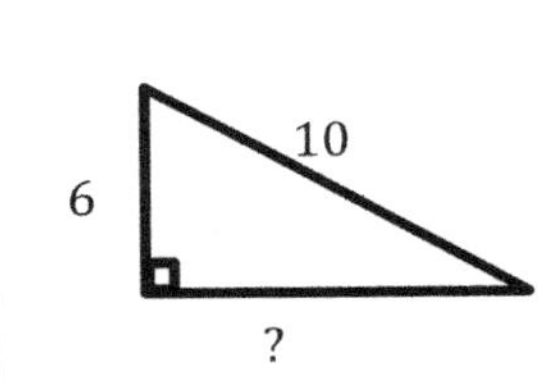

5)
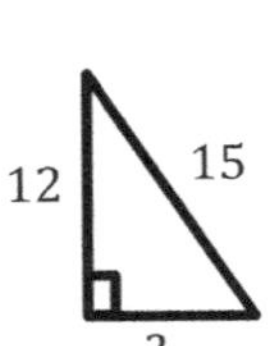

6)
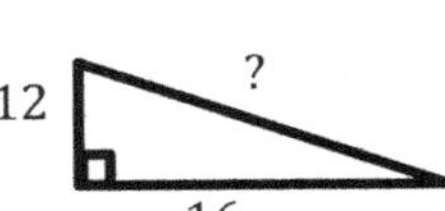

7)
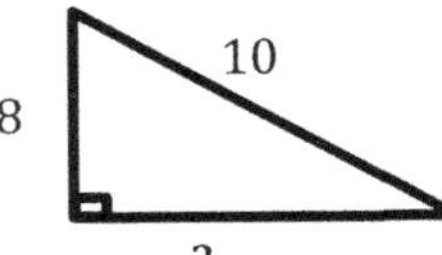

8)
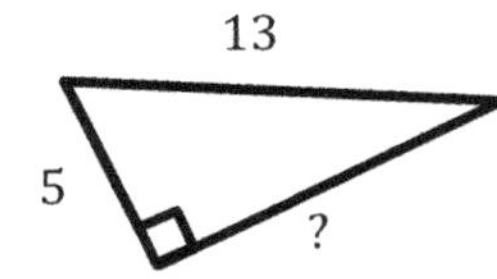

Triangles

Step-by-step guide:

- ✓ In any triangle the sum of all angles is 180 degrees.
- ✓ Area of a triangle = $\frac{1}{2}$ $(base \times height)$

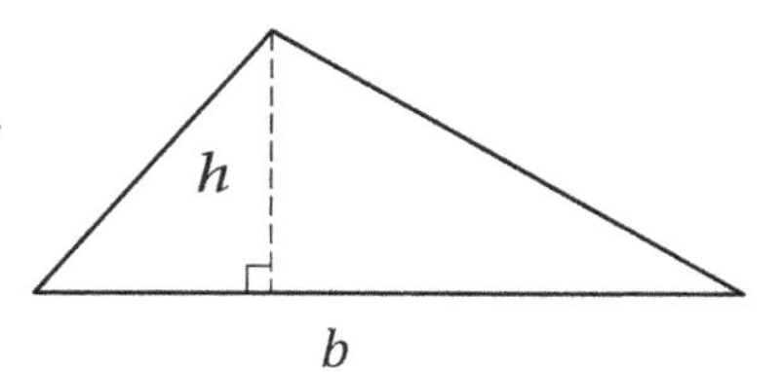

Example:

What is the area of triangles?

1)

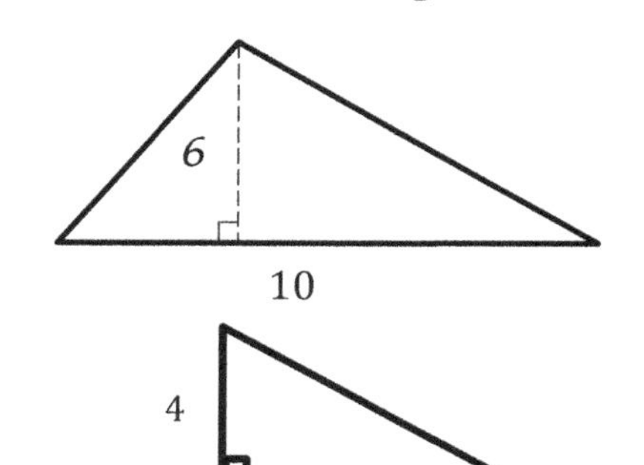

Solution:

Use the are formula: Area $= \frac{1}{2}\ (base \times height)$

$base = 10$ and $height = 6$

Area $= \frac{1}{2}(10 \times 6) = \frac{1}{2}(60) = 30$

2)

4

8

Solution:

Use the are formula: Area $= \frac{1}{2}\ (base \times height)$

$base = 8$ and $height = 4$

Area $= \frac{1}{2}(8 \times 4) = \frac{32}{2} = 16$

Find the measure of the unknown angle in each triangle.

1)

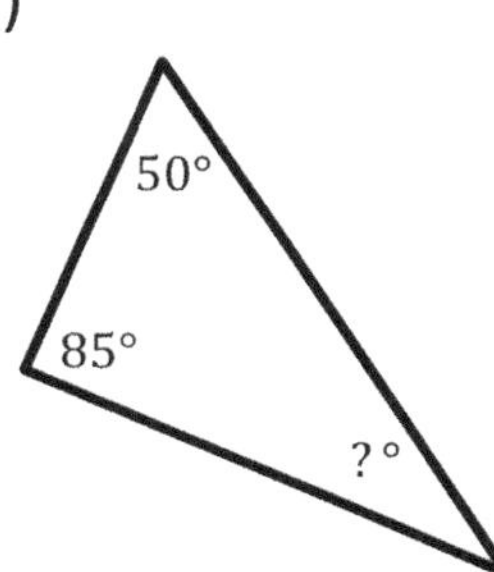

2)

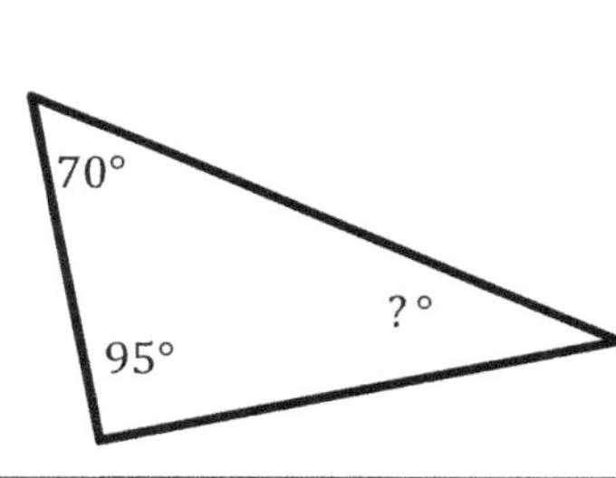

3)

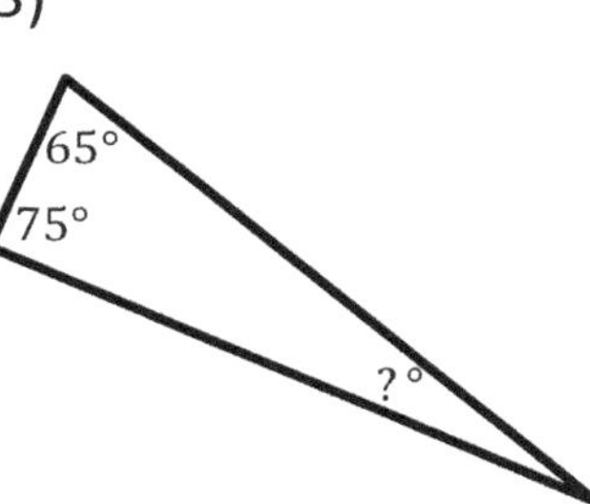

4)

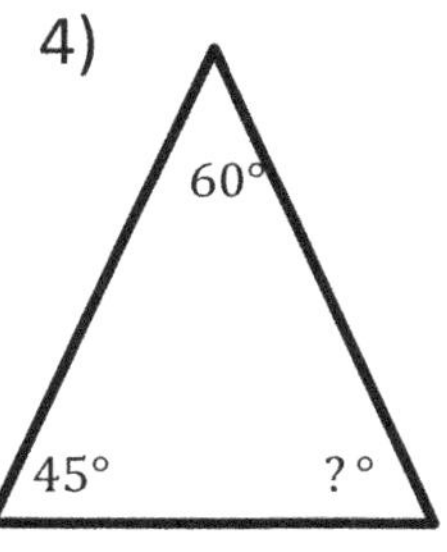

Find area of each triangle.

5)

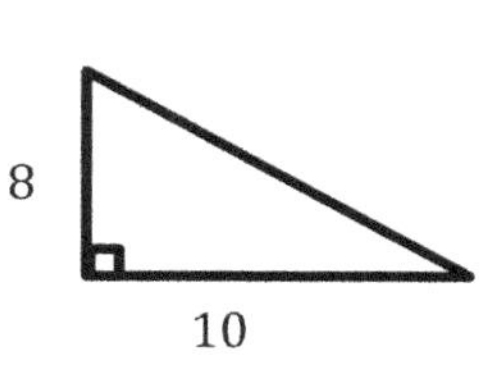

6)

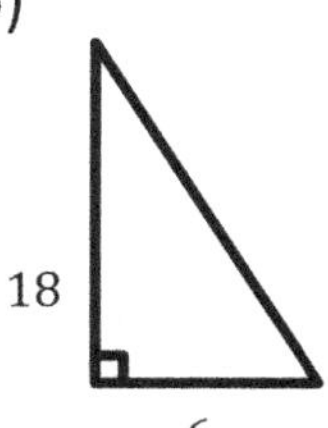

7)

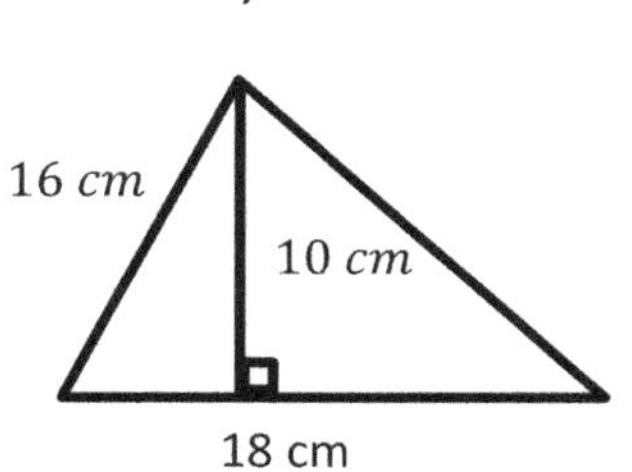

8)

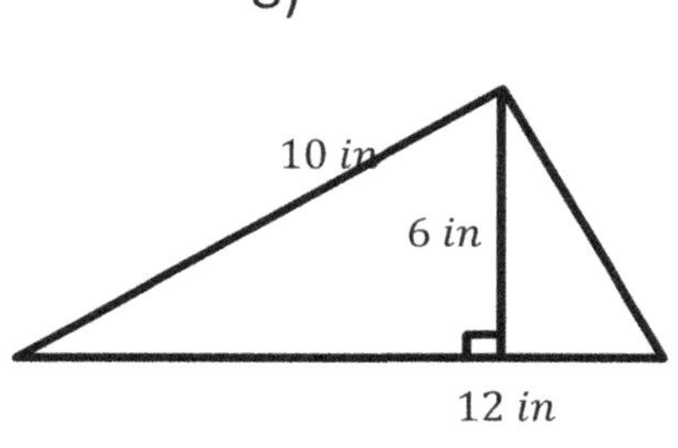

Polygons

Step-by-step guide:

Perimeter of a square $= 4 \times side = 4s$

s

Perimeter of a rectangle

$= 2(width + length)$

width

length

Perimeter of trapezoid

$= a + b + c + d$

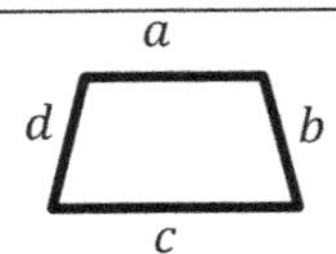

Perimeter of a regular hexagon $= 6a$

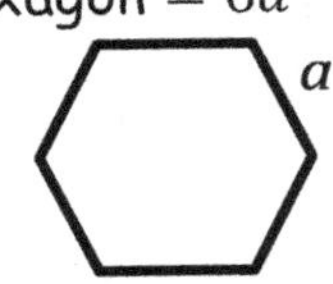

Example: Find the perimeter of following regular hexagon.

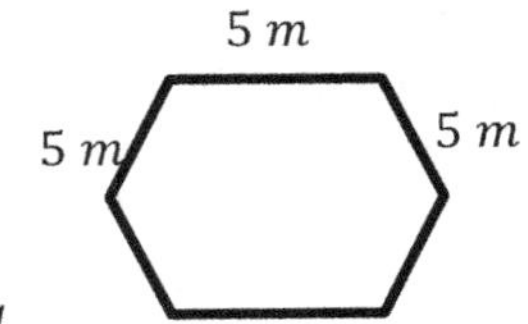

Perimeter of Pentagon $= 6a$

Perimeter of Pentagon $= 6a = 6 \times 5 = 30\ m$

Perimeter of a parallelogram $= 2(l + w)$

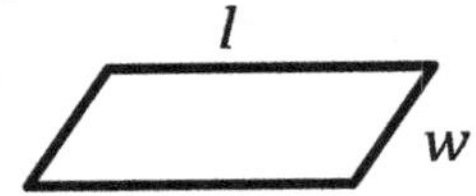

Find the perimeter of each shape.

1)

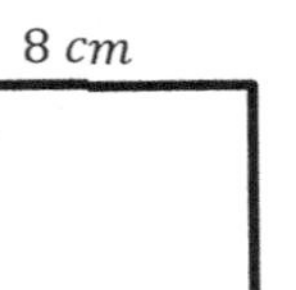

2)

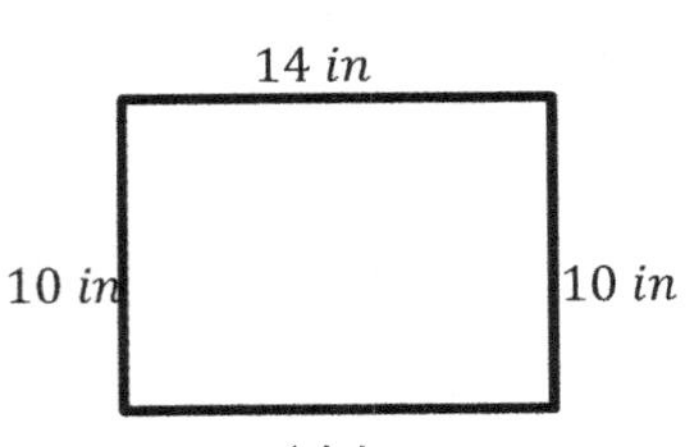

3)

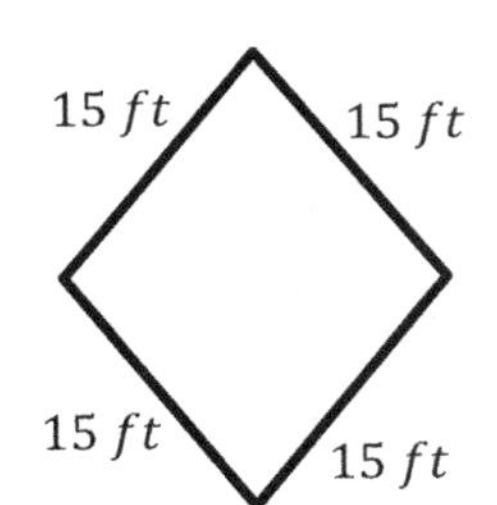

4)

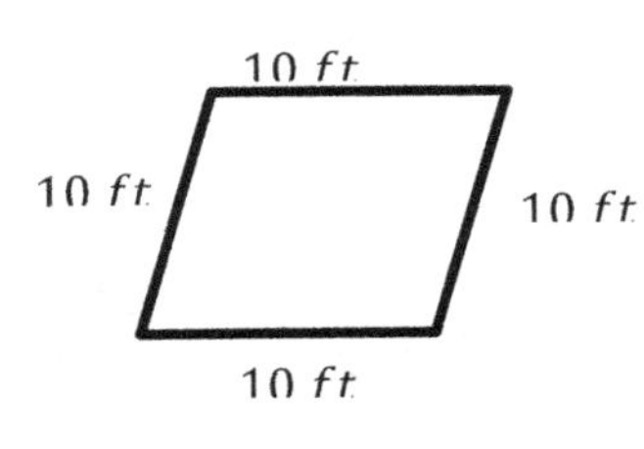

5) Regular hexagon

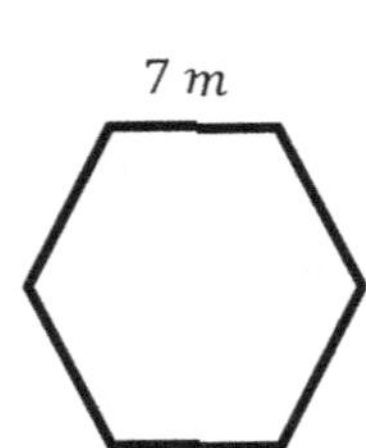

6)

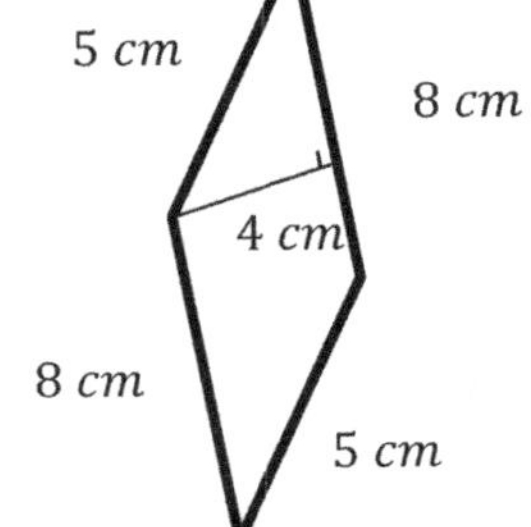

7) Parallelogram

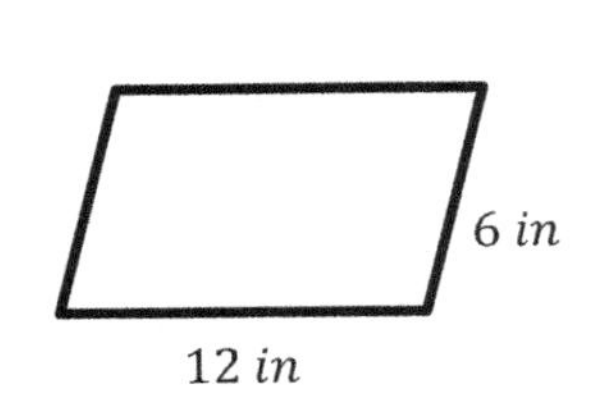

8) Square

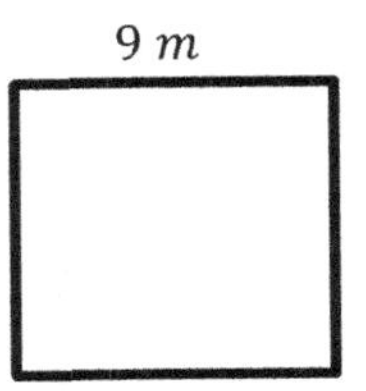

Circles

Step-by-step guide:

- ✓ In a circle, variable r is usually used for the radius and d for diameter and π is about 3.14.
- ✓ $Area\ of\ a\ circle = \pi r^2$
- ✓ $Circumference\ of\ a\ circle = 2\pi r$

Example:

1) Find the area of the circle.

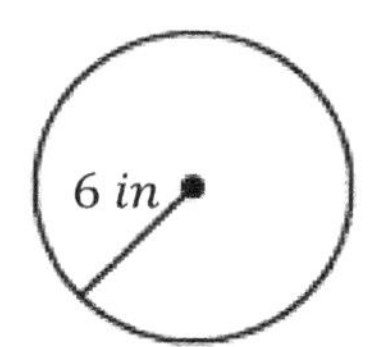

Use area formula: $Area = \pi r^2$,

$r = 6\ in$ then: $Area = \pi(6)^2 = 36\pi$, $\pi = 3.14$ then: $Area = 36 \times 3.14 = 113.04\ in^2$

2) Find the Circumference of the circle.

Use Circumference formula: $Circumference = 2\pi r$

$r = 9\ cm$, then: $Circumference = 2\pi(9) = 18\pi$

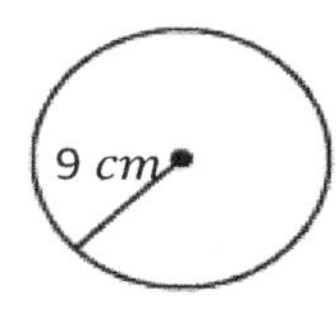

$\pi = 3.14$ then: $Circumference = 18 \times 3.14 = 56.52\ cm$

✍ ***Complete the table below.*** $(\pi = 3.14)$

	Radius	**Diameter**	**Circumference**	**Area**
Circle 1	4 *inches*	8 *inches*	25.12 *inches*	50.24 *square inches*
Circle 2		16 *meters*		
Circle 3				50.24 *square ft*
Circle 4			50.24 *miles*	
Circle 5		18 *kilometers*		
Circle 6	7 *centimeters*			
Circle 7		9 *feet*		
Circle 8				19.625 *square meters*

Trapezoids

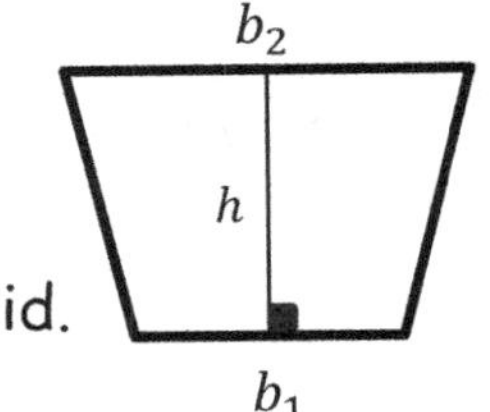

Step-by-step guide:

✓ A quadrilateral with at least one pair of parallel sides is a trapezoid.
✓ Area of a trapezoid $= \frac{1}{2}h(b_1 + b_2)$

Example:

Calculate the area of the trapezoid.

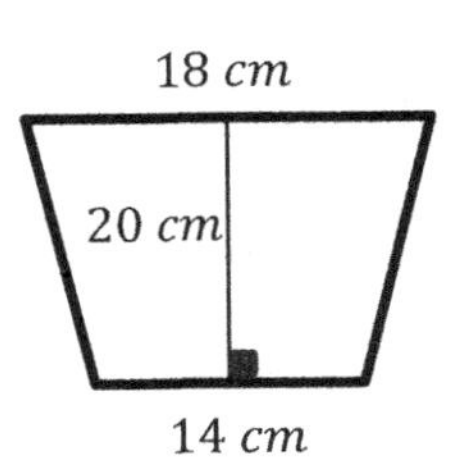

Use area formula: $A = \frac{1}{2}h(b_1 + b_2)$

$b_1 = 14\ cm$, $b_2 = 18\ cm$ and $h = 20\ cm$

Then: $A = \frac{1}{2}(20)(14 + 18) = 10(32) = 320\ cm^2$

Find the area of each trapezoid.

1)

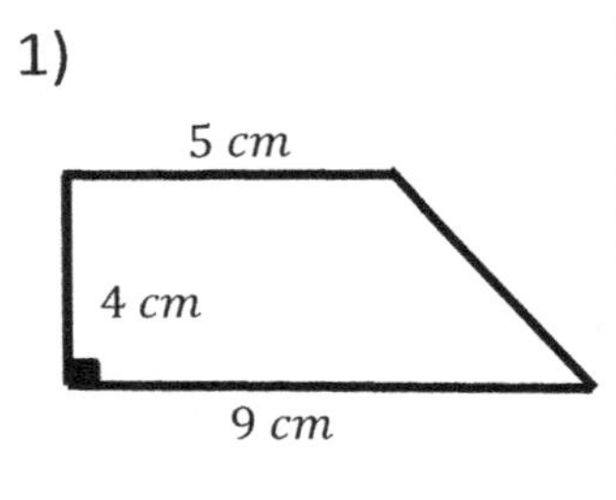

2)

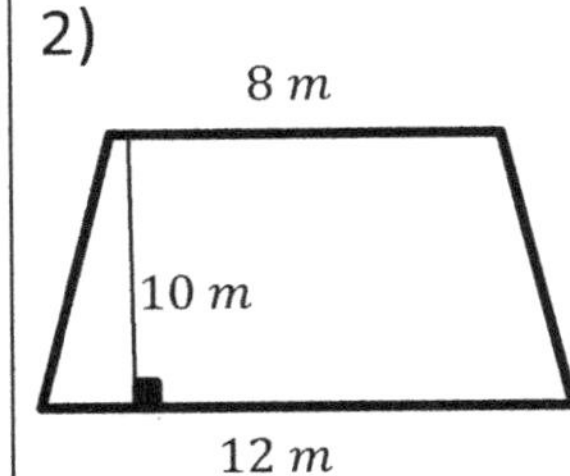

3)

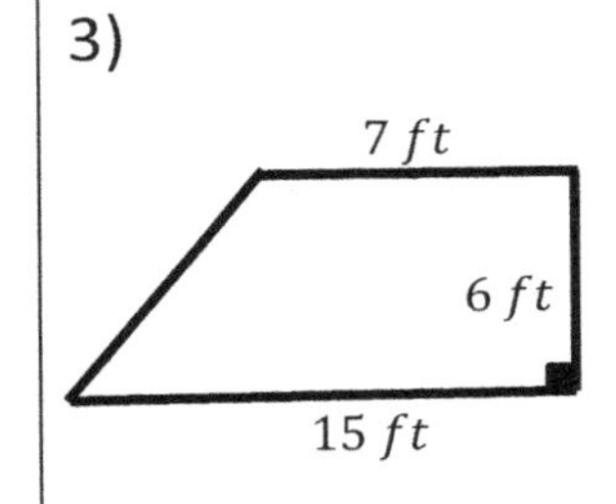

4)

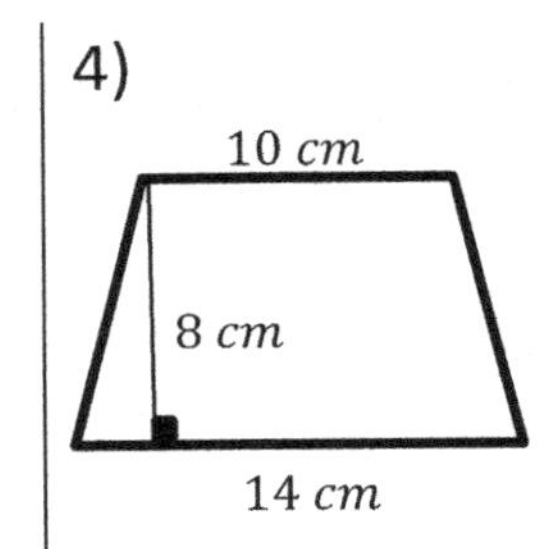

5)

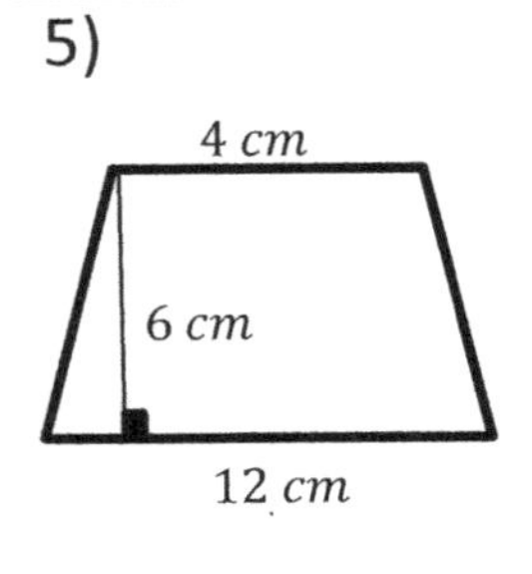

6)

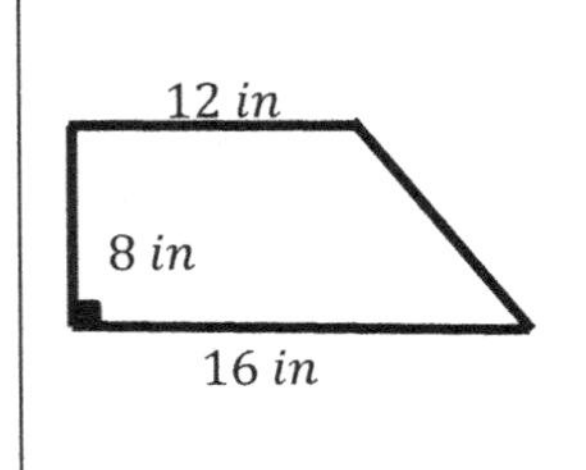

7)

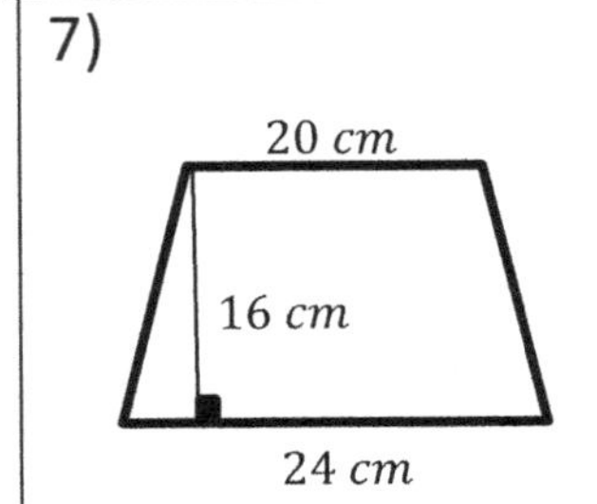

8)

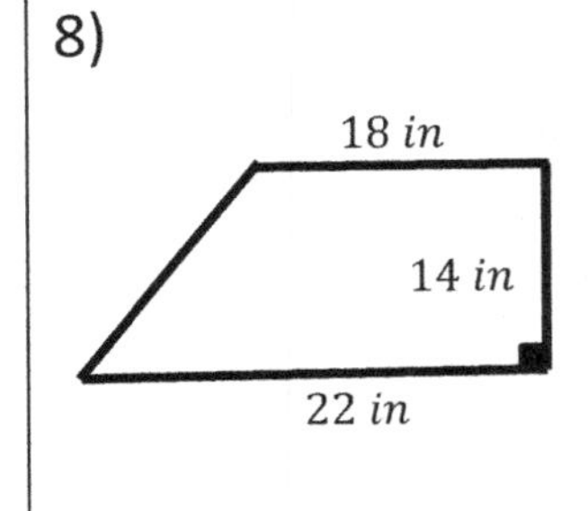

Cubes

Step-by-step guide:

- ✓ A cube is a three-dimensional solid object bounded by six square sides.
- ✓ Volume is the measure of the amount of space inside of a solid figure, like a cube, ball, cylinder or pyramid.
- ✓ Volume of a cube = $(\textbf{one side})^3$
- ✓ surface area of cube = $\mathbf{6} \times (\textbf{one side})^2$

Example:

Find the volume and surface area of this cube.

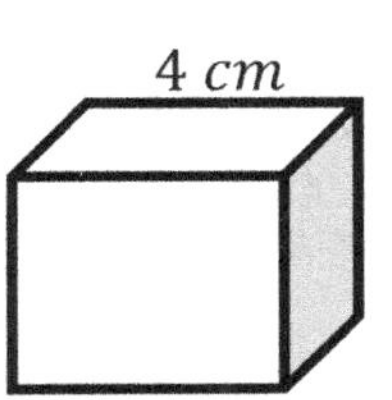

Use volume formula: $volume = (one\ side)^3$

Then: $volume = (one\ side)^3 = (4)^3 = 64\ cm^3$

Use surface area formula:

$surface\ area\ of\ cube: 6(one\ side)^2 = 6(4)^2 = 6(16) = 96\ cm^2$

✍ ***Find the volume of each cube.***

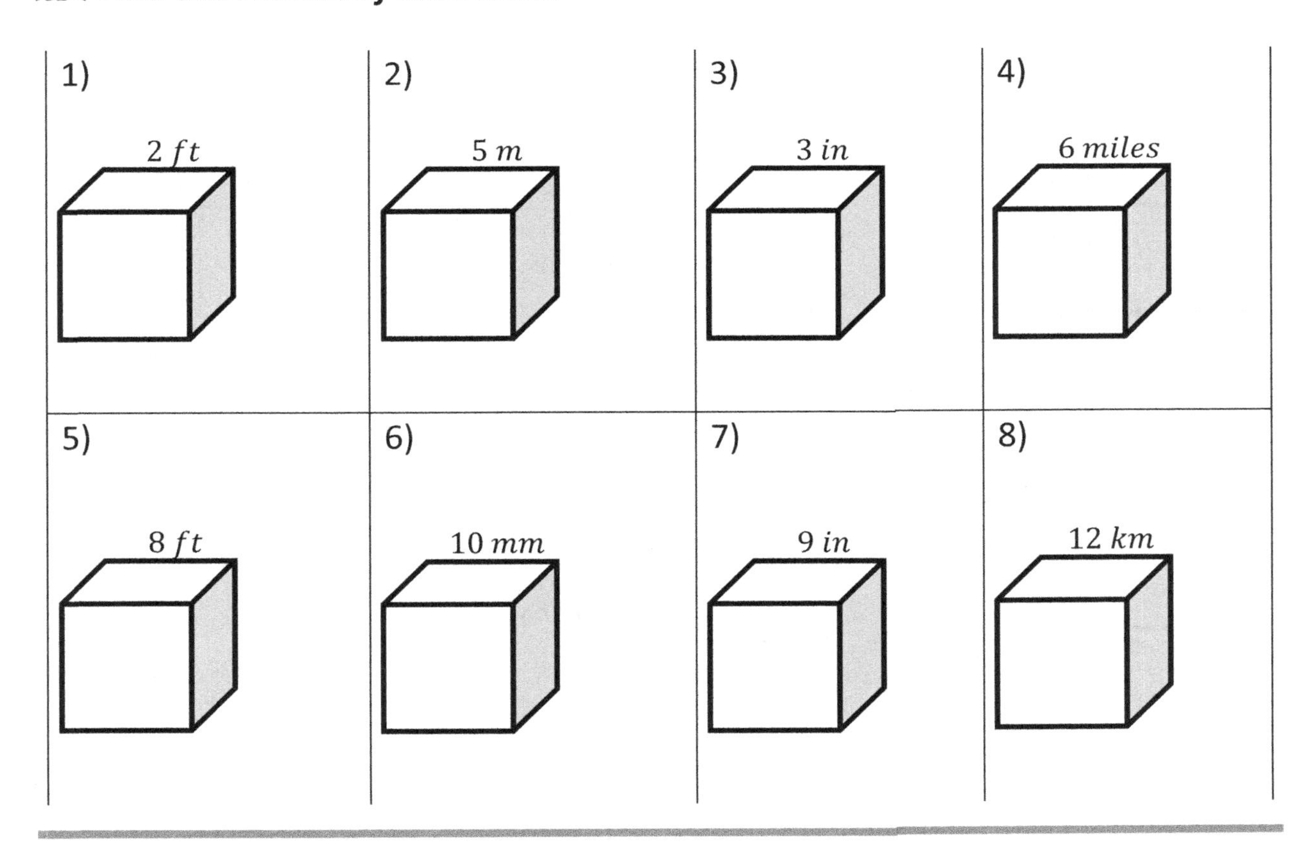

Rectangular Prisms

Step-by-step guide:

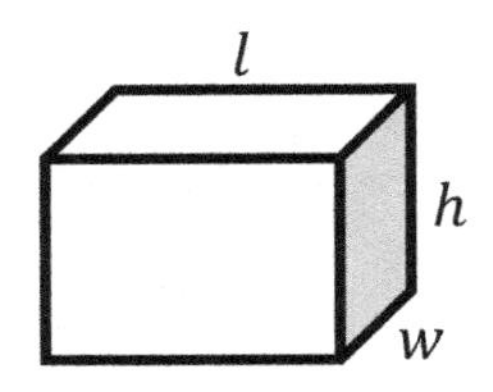

- ✓ A solid 3-dimensional object which has six rectangular faces.
- ✓ Volume of a Rectangular prism = $\boldsymbol{Length} \times \boldsymbol{Width} \times \boldsymbol{Height}$

$Volume = l \times w \times h$ $\quad$ $Surface\ area = 2(wh + lw + lh)$

Example:

Find the volume and surface area of rectangular prism.

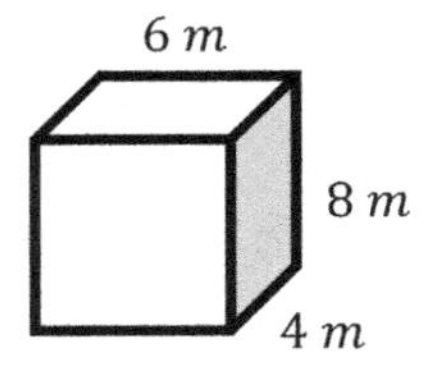

Use volume formula: $Volume = l \times w \times h$

Then: $Volume = 6 \times 4 \times 8 = 192\ m^3$

Use surface area formula: $Surface\ area = 2(wh + lw + lh)$

Then: $Surface\ area = 2\big((4 \times 8) + (6 \times 4) + (6 \times 8)\big)$

$$= 2(32 + 24 + 48) = 2(104) = 208\ m^2$$

✍ ***Find the volume of each Rectangular Prism.***

1)

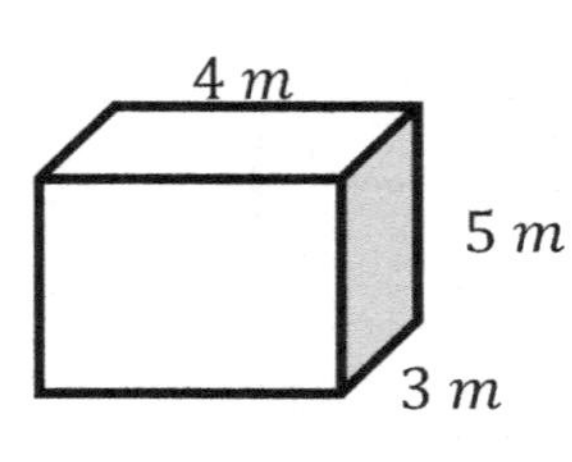

2)

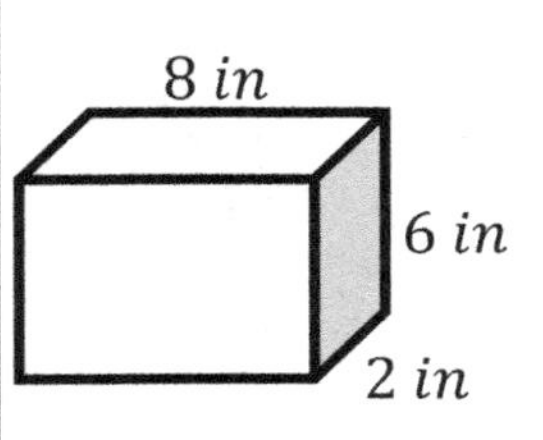

3)

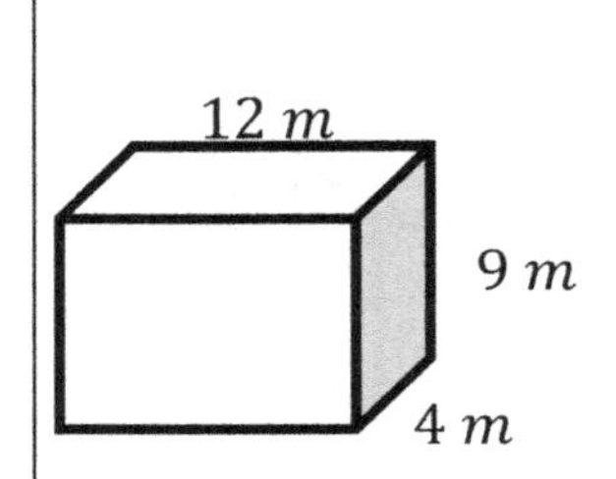

4)

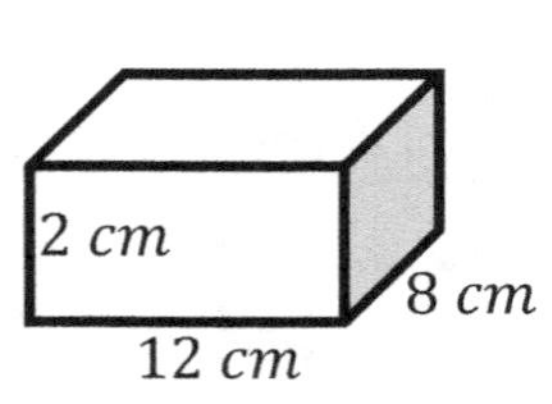

5)

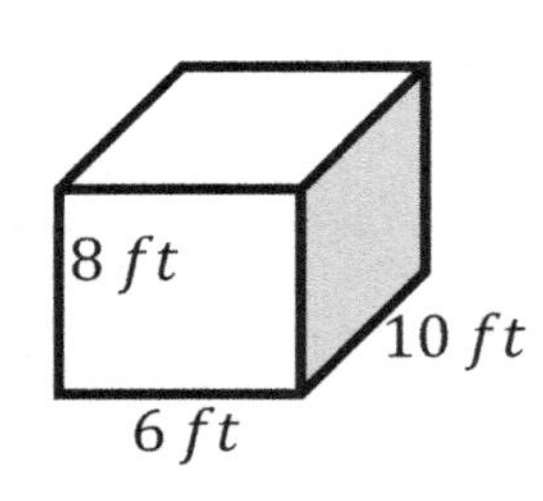

6)

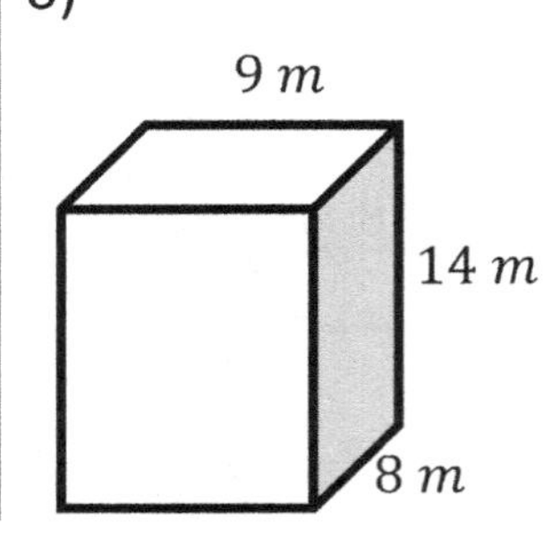

Cylinder

Step-by-step guide:

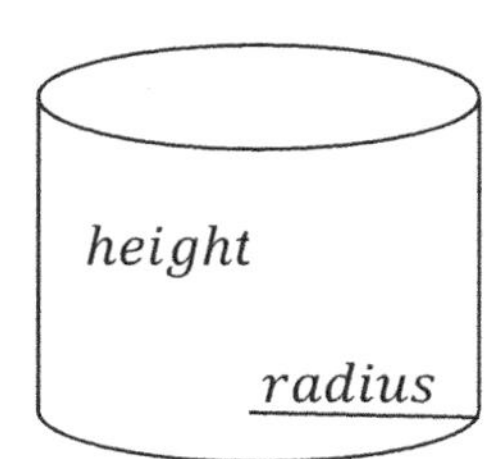

- ✓ A cylinder is a solid geometric figure with straight parallel sides and a circular or oval cross section.
- ✓ $Volume\ of\ Cylinder\ Formula = \pi(radius)^2 \times height \quad \pi = 3.14$
- ✓ $Surface\ area\ of\ a\ cylinder = 2\pi r^2 + 2\pi rh$

Example:

Find the volume and Surface area of the follow Cylinder.

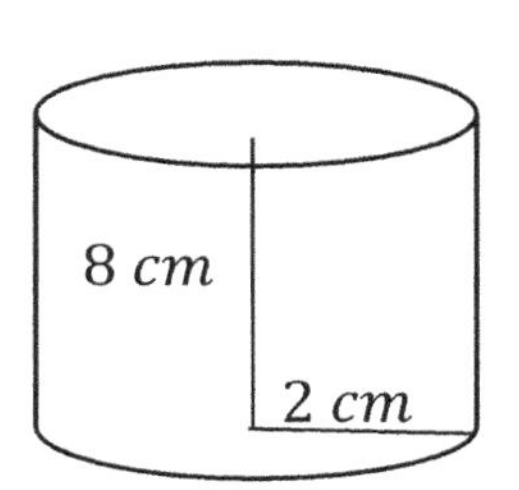

Use volume formula: $Volume = \pi(radius)^2 \times height$

Then: $Volume = \pi(2)^2 \times 8 = \pi 4 \times 8 = 32\pi$

$\pi = 3.14$ then: $Volume = 32\pi = 100.48\ cm^3$

Use surface area formula: $Surface\ area = 2\pi r^2 + 2\pi rh$

Then: $= 2\pi(2)^2 + 2\pi(2)(8) = 2\pi(4) + 2\pi(16) = 8\pi + 32\pi = 40\pi$

$\pi = 3.14$ then: $Surface\ area = 40 \times 3.14 = 125.6\ cm^2$

✍ ***Find the volume of each Cylinder. Round your answer to the nearest tenth.*** $(\pi = 3.14)$

1)

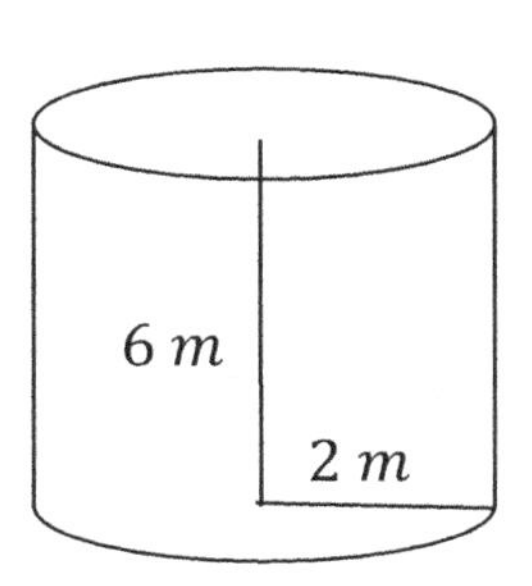

2)

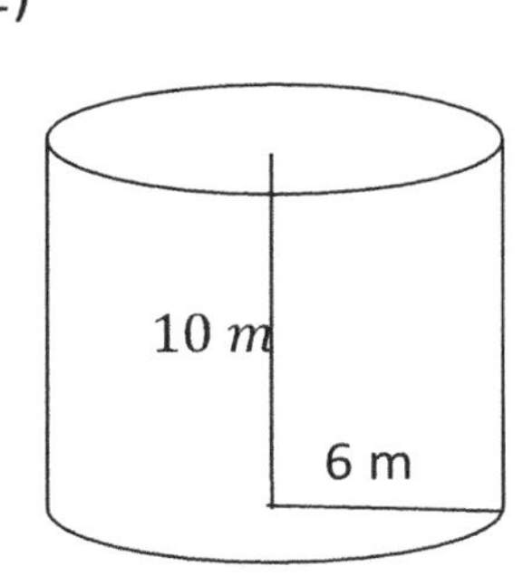

3)

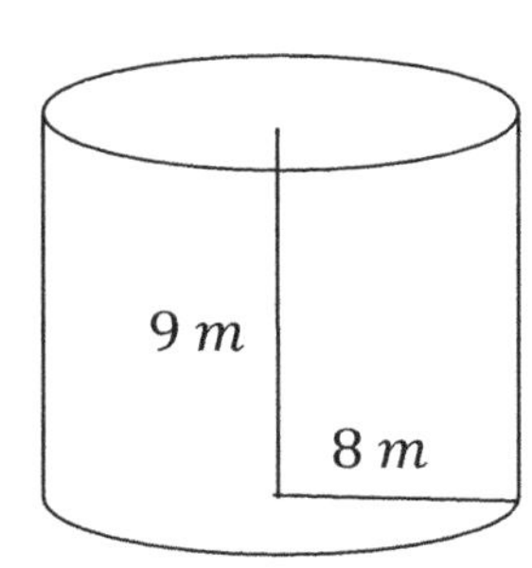

4)

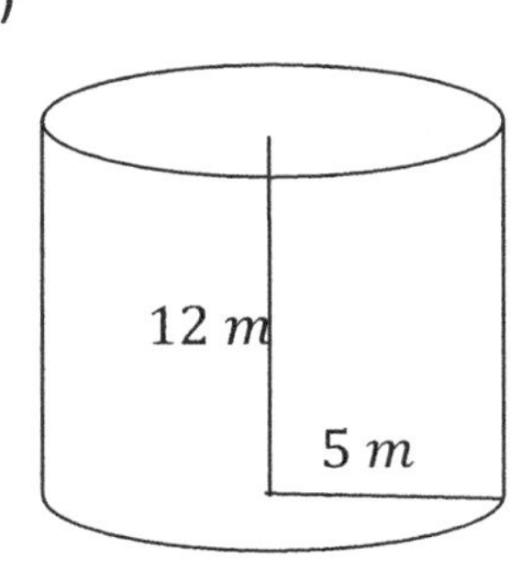

5)

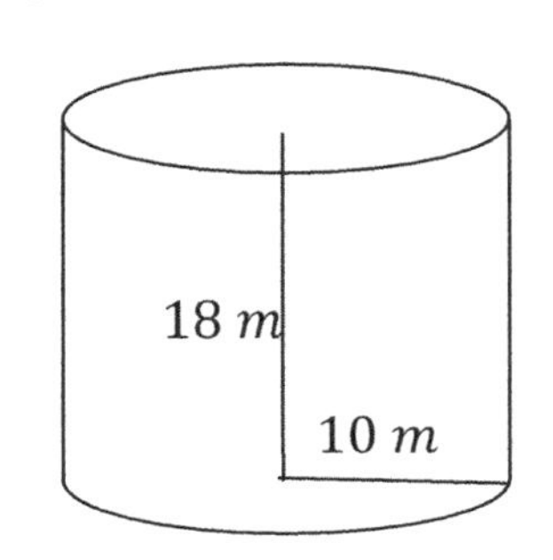

6)

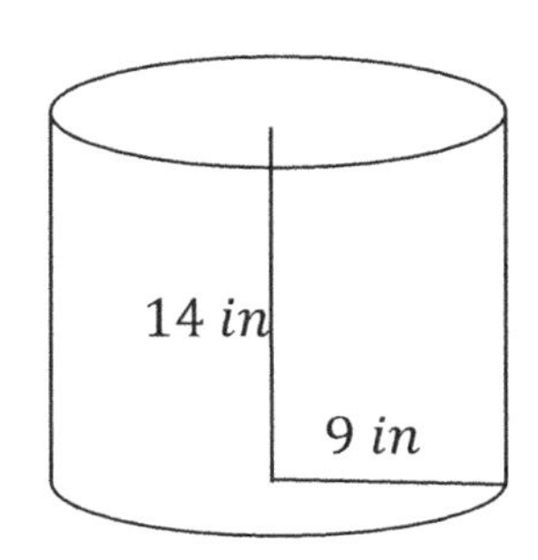

Answers – Chapter 11

The Pythagorean Theorem

1) 13
2) 5
3) 15
4) 8
5) 9
6) 20
7) 6
8) 12

Triangles

1) $45°$
2) $15°$
3) $40°$
4) $75°$
5) 40 *square unites*
6) 54 *square unites*
7) 90 *square unites*
8) 36 *square unites*

Polygons

1) $32\ cm$
2) $48\ in$
3) $60\ ft$
4) $40\ ft$
5) $42\ m$
6) $26\ cm$
7) $36\ in$
8) $36\ m$

Circles

	Radius	Diameter	Circumference	Area
Circle 1	4 *inches*	8 *inches*	25.12 *inches*	50.24 *square inches*
Circle 2	8 *meters*	16 *meters*	50.24 *meters*	200.96 *square meters*
Circle 3	4 *ft*	8 *ft*	25.12 *ft*	50.24 *square ft*
Circle 4	8 *miles*	16 *miles*	50.24 *miles*	200.96 *square miles*
Circle 5	9 *kilometers*	18 *kilometers*	56.52 *kilometers*	254.34 *sq. kilometers*
Circle 6	7 *centimeters*	14 *centimeters*	43.96 *centimeters*	153.86 *sq. centimeters*
Circle 7	4.5 *feet*	9 *feet*	28.26 *feet*	63.585 *square feet*
Circle 8	2.5 *meters*	5 *meters*	15.7 *meters*	19.625 *square meters*

Trapezoids

1) $28\ cm^2$
2) $100\ m^2$
3) $66\ ft^2$
4) $96\ cm^2$
5) $48\ cm^2$
6) $112\ in^2$
7) $352\ cm^2$
8) $280\ in^2$

Cubes

1) $8\ ft^3$
2) $125\ m^3$
3) $27\ in^3$
4) $216\ miles^3$
5) $512\ ft^3$
6) $1{,}000\ mm^3$
7) $729\ in^3$
8) $1{,}728\ km^3$

Rectangle Prisms

1) $60\ m^3$
2) $96\ in^3$
3) $432\ m^3$
4) $192\ cm^3$
5) $480\ ft^3$
6) $1{,}008\ m^3$

Cylinder

1) $75.36\ m^3$
2) $1{,}130.4\ m^3$
3) $1{,}808.64\ m^3$
4) $942\ m^3$
5) $5.652\ m^3$
6) $3{,}560.76\ in^3$

Chapter 12: Statistics and Probability

Math Topics that you'll learn in this chapter:

- ✓ Mean, Median, Mode, and Range of the Given Data
- ✓ Histograms
- ✓ Pie Graph
- ✓ Probability

Mean, Median, Mode, and Range of the Given Data

Step-by-step guide:

- ✓ Mean: $\frac{\text{sum of the data}}{\text{total number of data entires}}$
- ✓ Mode: value in the list that appears most often
- ✓ Range: the difference of largest value and smallest value in the list

Example:

1) What is the mode of these numbers? $18, 12, 8, 5, 3, 2, 0, 2$

   Mode: value in the list that appears most often
   Therefore: mode is 2

2) What is the median of these numbers? $2, 7, 11, 6, 13, 16, 3$

   Write the numbers in order: $2, 3, 6, 7, 11, 13, 16$

   Median is the number in the middle. Therefore, the median is 7.

Solve.

1) Eva went to shop and bought 4 apples, 6 peaches, 3 bananas, 5 pineapple and 8 melons. What are the Mean and Median of her purchase? ____________________

2) In a javelin throw competition, five athletics score 43, 45, 52, 58 and 62 meters. What are their Mean and Median? ____________________

Find Mode and Rage of the Given Data.

3) $6, 4, 8, 11, 2, 3$

   Mode: _____ Range: _____

4) $5, 7, 3, 12, 7, 10, 6, 9, 4$

   Mode: _____ Range: _____

5) $10, 10, 6, 7, 10, 7, 13, 15$

   Mode: _____ Range: _____

6) $8, 7, 4, 7, 5, 4, 12, 7$

   Mode: _____ Range: _____

Histograms

Step-by-step guide:

✓ A histogram is an accurate representation of the distribution of numerical data.

Example:

Use the following Graph to complete the table.

Day	Distance (km)
1	
2	

→

Answer:

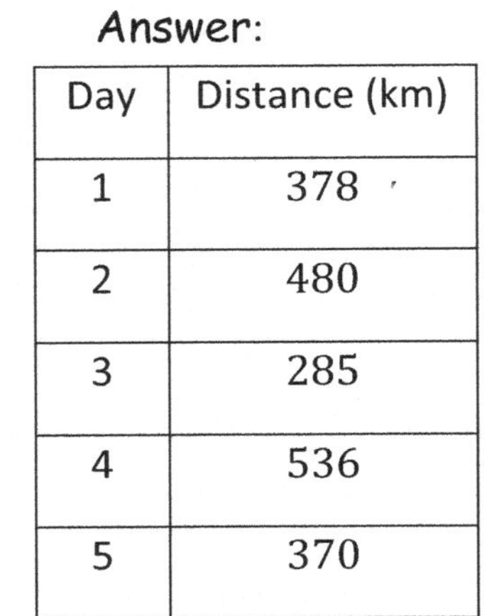

Day	Distance (km)
1	378
2	480
3	285
4	536
5	370

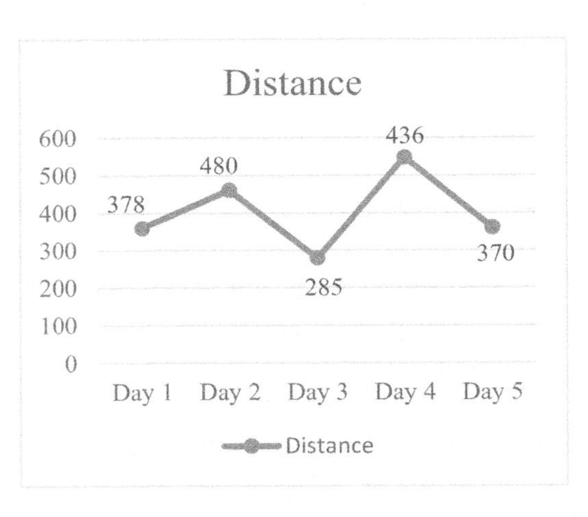

The following table shows the number of births in the US from 2007 to 2012 (in millions).

Year	Number of births (in millions)
2007	4.32
2008	4.25
2009	4.13
2010	4
2011	3.95
2012	3.95

Draw a histogram for the table.

Pie Graph

Step-by-step guide:

- ✓ A Pie Chart is a circle chart divided into sectors, each sector represents the relative size of each value.

Example:

A library has 670 books that include Mathematics, Physics, Chemistry, English and History. Use following graph to answer question.

What is the number of Mathematics books?

Number of total books $= 670$
Percent of Mathematics books $= 30\% = 0.30$
Then: $0.30 \times 670 = 201$

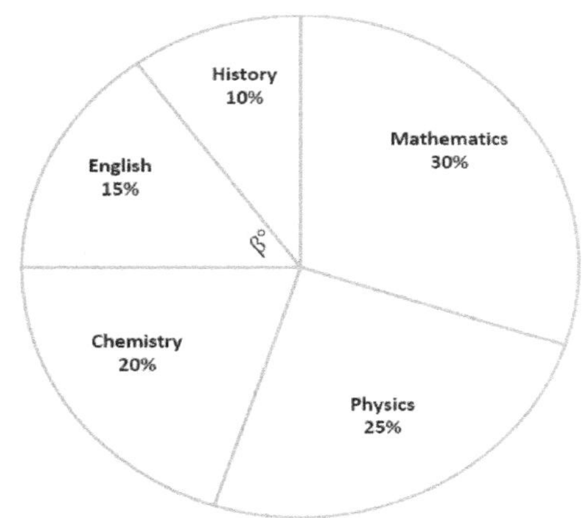

The circle graph below shows all Jason's expenses for last month. Jason spent $400 on his bills last month.

1) How much did Jason spend on his car last month? ________

2) How much did Jason spend for foods last month? ________

3) How much did Jason spend on his rent last month? ______

4) What fraction is Jason's expenses for his bills and Car out of his total expenses last month?

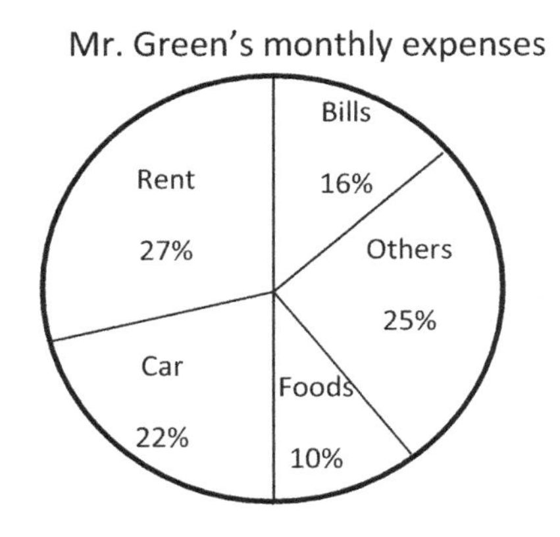

Probability Problems

Step-by-step guide:

- ✓ Probability is the likelihood of something happening in the future. It is expressed as a number between zero (can never happen) to 1 (will always happen).
- ✓ Probability can be expressed as a fraction, a decimal, or a percent.

Example:

1) If there are 8 red balls and 12 blue balls in a basket, what is the probability that John will pick out a red ball from the basket?
   There are 8 red ball and 20 are total number of balls. Therefore, probability that John will pick out a red ball from the basket is 8 out of 20 or $\frac{8}{8+12}=\frac{8}{20}=\frac{2}{5}$.
2) A bag contains 18 balls: two green, five black, eight blue, a brown, a red and one white. If 17 balls are removed from the bag at random, what is the probability that a brown ball has been removed?
   If 17 balls are removed from the bag at random, there will be one ball in the bag.
   The probability of choosing a brown ball is 1 out of 18. Therefore, the probability of not choosing a brown ball is 17 out of 18 and the probability of having not a brown ball after removing 17 balls is the same.

Solve.

1) A number is chosen at random from 1 to 10. Find the probability of selecting number 4 or smaller numbers. ________________

2) Bag A contains 9 red marbles and 3 green marbles. Bag B contains 9 black marbles and 6 orange marbles. What is the probability of selecting a green marble at random from bag A? What is the probability of selecting a black marble at random from Bag B? __________ ______________

Answers – Chapter 12

Mean, Median, Mode, and Range of the Given Data

1) Mean: 5.2, Median: 5
2) Mean: 52, Median: 52
3) Mode: –, Range: 9
4) Mode: 7, Range: 9
5) Mode: 10, Range: 9
6) Mode: 7, Range: 8

Histograms

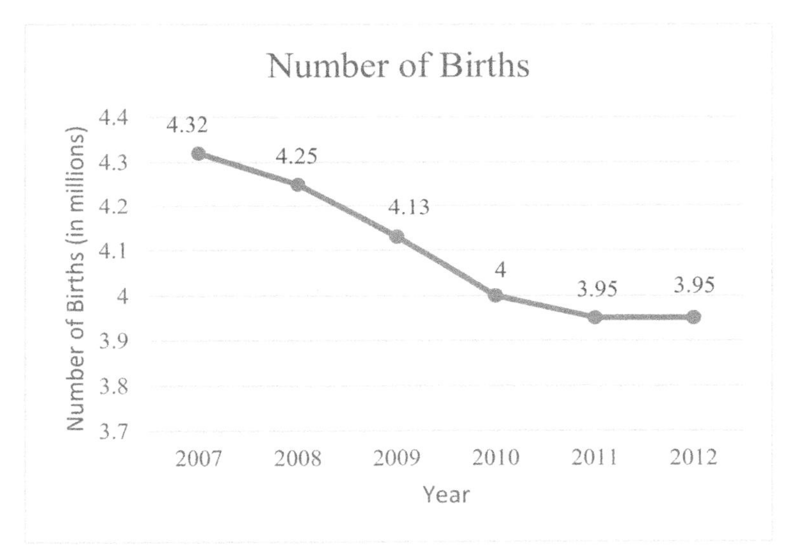

Pie Graph

1) \$550
2) \$250
3) \$675
4) $\frac{19}{50}$

Probability Problems

1) $\frac{2}{5}$
2) $\frac{1}{4}, \frac{3}{5}$

Chapter 13: Measurements

Math Topics that you'll learn in this chapter:

- ✓ Convert Measurement Units
- ✓ Distance Measurement
- ✓ Weight Measurement

Convert Measurement Units

Step-by-step guide:

- ✓ $1\ inch = 2.5\ cm$
- ✓ $1\ foot = 12\ inches$
- ✓ $1\ yard = 3\ feet$
- ✓ $1\ yard = 36\ inches$
- ✓ $1\ inch = 0.0254\ m$

Example:

1) Convert 10 inches to cm.

   $1\ inch = 2.5\ cm$

   Then: $10 \times 2.5 = 25$

2) Convert 144 inches to yard.

   $1\ yard = 36\ inches$

   Then: $\frac{144}{36} = 4$

Convert to an appropriate measurement unit. (Round to the nearest Hundredths)

1) $4\ feet = \_\_\_\_\ inches$
2) $8\ inches = \_\_\_\_\ foot$
3) $10\ feet = \_\_\_\_\ m$
4) $15\ cm = \_\_\_\_\ m$
5) $5\ inches = \_\_\_\_\ cm$
6) $10\ inches = \_\_\_\_\ m$
7) $15\ inches = \_\_\_\_\ cm$
8) $12\ inches = \_\_\_\_\ m$
9) $8\ feet = \_\_\_\_\ inches$
10) $25\ cm = \_\_\_\_\ inches$
11) $11\ inches = \_\_\_\_\ cm$
12) $80\ inches = \_\_\_\_\ m$

Distance Measurement

Step-by-step guide:

- ✓ $\mathbf{1\ mile = 5,280\ ft}$
- ✓ $\mathbf{1\ mile = 1,760\ yd}$
- ✓ $\mathbf{1\ mile = 1,609.34\ m}$

Example:

1) Convert 5 miles to ft.

$1\ mile = 5{,}280\ ft$

Then: $5 \times 5{,}280 = 26{,}400$

2) Convert 8 miles to yd.

$1\ miles = 1{,}760$

Then: $8 \times 1{,}760 = 14{,}080$

Convert to the new units. (Round to the nearest Hundredths)

1) $10\ mi =$ ______ yd
2) $9\ mi =$ ______ yd
3) $12\ mi =$ ______ yd
4) $10\ mi =$ ______ ft
5) $15\ mi =$ ______ ft
6) $20\ mi =$ ______ yd
7) $16\ mi =$ ______ yd
8) $2\ mi =$ ______ ft
9) $21\ mi =$ ______ ft
10) $6\ mi =$ ______ ft
11) $3\ mi =$ ______ yd
12) $72\ mi =$ ______ ft

Weight Measurement

Step-by-step guide:

✓ $\mathbf{1\ kg = 1000g}$

Example:

1) Convert 500 gram to kg.

   $1\ kg = 1{,}000\ g$

   Then: $\frac{500}{1{,}000} = 0.5$

2) Convert 6 kg to g.

   $1\ kg = 1{,}000\ g$

   Then: $6 \times 1{,}000 = 6{,}000$

Convert to grams.

1) $0.01\ kg =$ ________ g
2) $0.2\ kg =$ ________ g
3) $0.04\ kg =$ ________ g
4) $0.05\ kg =$ ________ g
5) $0.5\ kg =$ ________ g
6) $3.2\ kg =$ ________ g

Convert to kilograms.

7) $20{,}000\ g =$ ______ kg
8) $3{,}000\ g =$ ______ kg
9) $100{,}000\ g =$ ______ kg
10) $150{,}000\ g =$ ______ kg
11) $120{,}000\ g =$ ______ kg
12) $200{,}000\ g =$ ______ kg

Answers – Chapter 13

Convert Measurement Units

1) $4\ feet = 48\ inches$
2) $8\ inches = 0.67\ foot$
3) $10\ feet = 3.05\ m$
4) $15\ cm = 0.15\ m$
5) $5\ inches = 12.7\ cm$
6) $10\ inches = 0.25\ m$
7) $15\ inches = 38.1\ cm$
8) $12\ inches = 0.3\ m$
9) $8\ feet = 96\ inches$
10) $25\ cm = 9.84\ inches$
11) $11\ inch = 27.94\ cm$
12) $80\ inch = 2.03\ m$

Distance Measurement

1) $10\ mi = 17{,}600\ yd$
2) $9\ mi = 15{,}840\ yd$
3) $12\ mi = 21{,}120\ yd$
4) $10\ mi = 52{,}800\ ft$
5) $15\ mi = 79{,}200\ ft$
6) $20\ mi = 35{,}200\ yd$
7) $16\ mi = 28{,}160\ yd$
8) $21\ mi = 110{,}880\ ft$
9) $6\ mi = 31{,}680\ ft$
10) $3\ mi = 5{,}280\ yd$
11) $72\ mi = 380{,}160\ ft$
12) $41\ mi = 72{,}160\ yd$

Weight Measurement

1) $0.01\ kg = 10\ g$
2) $0.2\ kg = 200\ g$
3) $0.04\ kg = 40\ g$
4) $0.05\ kg = 50\ g$
5) $0.5\ kg = 500\ g$
6) $3.2\ kg = 3{,}200\ g$
7) $20{,}000\ g = 20\ kg$
8) $3{,}000\ g = 3\ kg$
9) $100{,}000\ g = 100\ kg$
10) $150{,}000\ g = 150\ kg$
11) $120{,}000\ g = 120\ kg$
12) $200{,}000\ g = 200\ kg$

STAAR Test Review

The State of Texas Assessments of Academic Readiness (STAAR) is developed under the supervision of the Texas Education Agency and is taken by all public school students in Texas, grades 3–12. The tests measure the progress of students from 3rd grade to 8th grade, as well as high school. STAAR is the state's testing program and is based on state curriculum standards in core subjects including:

- Reading,
- Writing,
- Mathematics,
- Science,
- Social Studies

In high school, students take end-of-course STAAR exams in five high school subjects:

- Algebra I,
- Biology,
- English I,
- English II,
- U.S. History.

Students take STAAR tests in the spring. The number of tests a student takes each year will depend on what grade he or she is in. Most students will have two to four testing days during a school year.

In this section, there are two complete Grade 6 STAAR Math Tests. Take these tests to see what score you'll be able to receive on a real STAAR Math test.

Good luck!

Time to refine your skill with a practice examination

Take a practice STAAR Math Test to simulate the test day experience. After you've finished, score your test using the answer key.

Before You Start

- You'll need a pencil and a calculator to take the test.
- There are two types of questions:

  Multiple choice questions: for each of these questions, there are four or more possible answers. Choose which one is best.

  Grid-ins questions: for these questions, write your answer in the box provided.
- It's okay to guess. You won't lose any points if you're wrong.
- The STAAR Mathematics test contains a formula sheet, which displays formulas relating to geometric measurement and certain algebra concepts. Formulas are provided to test-takers so that they may focus on application, rather than the memorization, of formulas.
- After you've finished the test, review the answer key to see where you went wrong and what areas you need to improve.

Good luck!

STAAR Mathematics
Practice Test 1

2020

Grade 6

Total number of questions: 40

Total time to complete the test: No time limit

You may use a calculator on this practice test.

STAAR Grade 6 Mathematics Reference Materials

AREA

Triangle	$A = \frac{1}{2}bh$
Rectangle Parallelogram	$A = bh$
Trapezoid	$A = \frac{1}{2}h\ (b_1 + b_2)$
Circle	$A = \pi r^2$

VOLUME

Rectangle Prism	$V = Bh$

LENGTH

Customary	Metric
1 mile = 1,760 yards (yd)	1 kilometer (km) = 1,000 meter (m)
1 yard = 3 feet (ft)	1 meter (m) = 100 centimeters (cm)
1 foot (ft) = 12 inches (in.)	1 centimeter (cm) = 10 millimeters (mm)

VOLUME AND CAPACITY

Customary	**Metric**
1 gallon (gal) = 4 quarts (qt)	1 liter (L) = 1,000 millimeters (mL)
1 quart (qt) = 2 pints (pt)	
1 pint (pt) = 2 cups (c)	
1 cup (c) = 8 fluid ounces (fl oz)	

WEIGHT AND MASS

Customary	**Metric**
1 ton (T) = 2,000 Pounds (lb)	1 kilogram (kg) = 1,000 grams (g)
1 pound (lb) = 16 ounces (oz)	1 gram (g) = 1,000 milligrams (mg)

1) $4(1.052) - 3.126 = \cdots?$
A. 0.926
B. 1.082
C. 1.122
D. 1.134

2) Which list shows the integer numbers listed in order from least to greatest?
A. $-12, -4, -1, -2, 1, 3, 7$
B. $-12, -1, -2, -4, 1, 3, 7$
C. $-12, -4, -2, -1, 1, 3, 7$
D. $-1, -2, -4, -12, 1, 3, 7$

3) There are 55 blue marbles and 143 red marbles. We want to place these marbles in some boxes so that there is the same number of red marbles in each box and the same number of blue marbles in each of the box. How many boxes do we need?
A. 8
B. 9
C. 10
D. 11

4) What is the value of the following expression?

$$2{,}205 \div 315$$

A. 5
B. 6
C. 7
D. 8

5) Solve the following equation.

$$112 = 22 + x$$

A. $x = -90$
B. $x = 90$
C. $x = -134$
D. $x = 134$

6) Car A travels 221.5 km at a given time, while car B travels 1.2 times the distance car A travels at the same time. What is the distance car B travels during that time?
A. $222.7\ km$
B. $233.5\ km$
C. $241.5\ km$
D. $265.8\ km$

7) The perimeter of the trapezoid below is 38. What is its area?

A. $198\ cm^2$
B. $162\ cm^2$
C. $99\ cm^2$
D. $81\ cm^2$

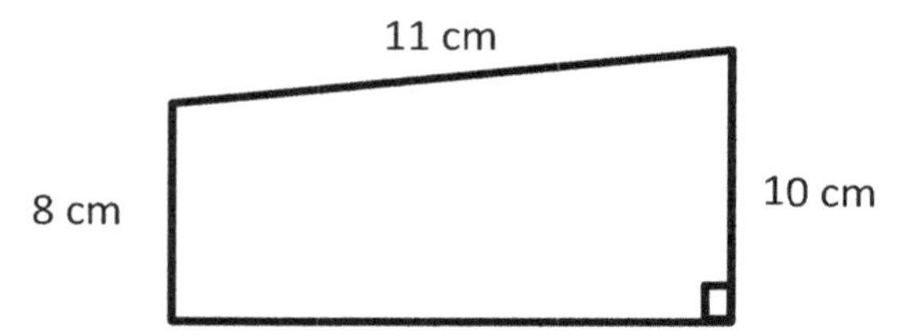

8) Which of the following expressions has the greatest value?
A. $3^1 + 12$
B. $3^3 - 3^2$
C. $3^4 - 60$
D. $3^5 - 218$

9) The diameter of a circle is π. What is the area of the circle?
A. $2\pi^2$
B. π^2
C. $\frac{\pi^3}{3}$
D. $\frac{\pi^3}{4}$

10) Alfred has x apples. Alvin has 40 apples, which is 15 apples less than number of apples Alfred owns. If Baron has $\frac{1}{5}$ times as many apples as Alfred has. How many apples does Baron have?
A. 5
B. 11
C. 55
D. 275

11) In the following triangle find α.
A. $100°$
B. $90°$
C. $60°$
D. $30°$

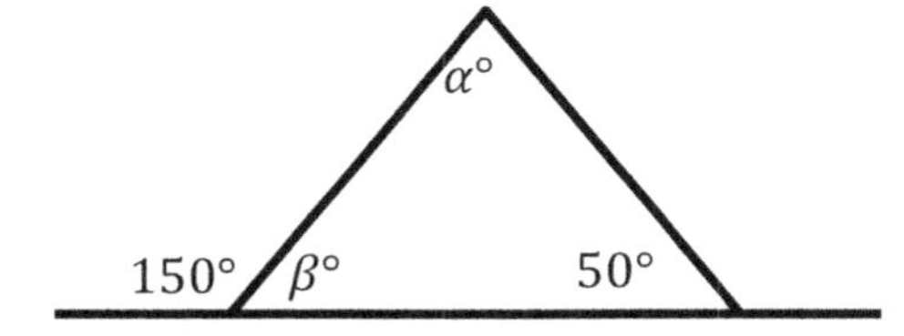

12) The price of a laptop is decreased by 15% to \$425. What is its original price?
A. \$283
B. \$430
C. \$500
D. \$550

13) Find the perimeter of shape in the following figure? (all angles are right angles)

A. 21
B. 22
C. 24
D. 20

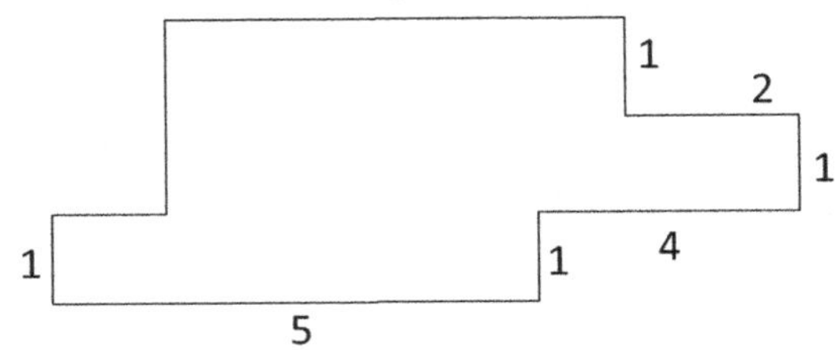

14) What is the probability of choosing a month starts with A in a year?

A. 1
B. $\frac{2}{3}$
C. $\frac{1}{2}$
D. $\frac{1}{6}$

15) What are the values of mode and median in the following set of numbers?

$$1, 3, 3, 6, 6, 5, 4, 3, 1, 1, 2$$

A. $Mode: 1, 2, Median: 2$
B. $Mode: 1, 3, Median: 3$
C. $Mode: 2, 3, Median: 2$
D. $Mode: 1, 3, Median: 2.5$

16) Which expression equivalent to $x \times 92$?

A. $(x \times 90) + 2$
B. $x \times 9 \times 2$
C. $(x \times 90) + (x \times 2)$
D. $(x \times 90) + 2$

17) The ratio of pens to pencils in a box is 3 to 5. If there are 96 pens and pencils in the box altogether, how many more pens should be put in the box to make the ratio of pens to pencils $1 : 1$?

A. 22
B. 23
C. 24
D. 25

18) If point A placed at $-\frac{24}{3}$ on a number line, which of the following points has a distance equal to 5 from point A?

A. -13
B. -3
C. -2
D. A and B

19) Which of the following shows the numbers in increasing order?

A. $\frac{3}{13}, \frac{4}{11}, \frac{5}{14}, \frac{2}{5}$
B. $\frac{3}{13}, \frac{5}{14}, \frac{4}{11}, \frac{2}{5}$
C. $\frac{3}{13}, \frac{5}{14}, \frac{2}{5}, \frac{4}{11}$
D. $\frac{5}{14}, \frac{3}{13}, \frac{2}{5}, \frac{4}{11}$

20) If $x = -4$, which of the following equations is true?

A. $x(3x - 1) = 50$
B. $5(11 - x^2) = -25$
C. $3(-2x + 5) = 49$
D. $x(-5x - 19) = -3$

21) What is the missing prime factor of number 450?

$$450 = 2^1 \times 3^2 \times \ldots$$

Write your answer in the box below?

22) What is the perimeter of the following shape? (it's a right triangle)

A. $14\ cm$
B. $18\ cm$
C. $24\ cm$
D. $32\ cm$

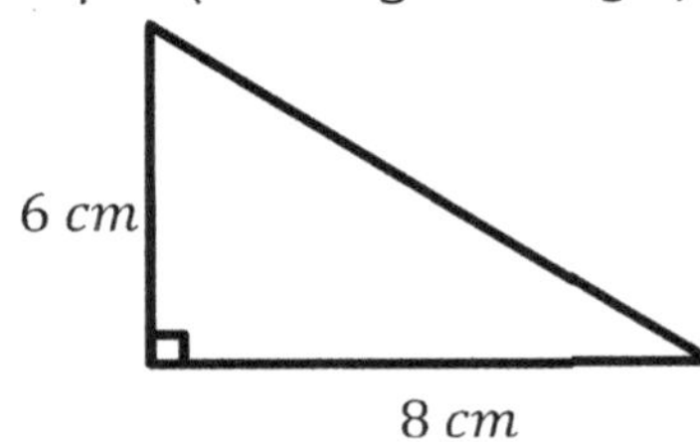

23) 65 is what percent of 50?
A. 50%
B. 77%
C. 130%
D. 140%

24) Which of the following expressions has a value of -23?
A. $-10+(-8)+\frac{-5}{2}\times 2$
B. $5\times 3+(-2)\times 18$
C. $-10+6\times 8\div(-4)$
D. $(-3)\times(-7)+2$

25) 300 inches equal to …?
A. $3600\ ft.$
B. $900\ ft.$
C. $100\ ft.$
D. $25\ ft.$

26) Which of the following equations is true?
A. $0.09=\frac{9}{10}$
B. $\frac{20}{100}=0.02$
C. $2.4=\frac{24}{10}$
D. $\frac{35}{7}=0.5$

27) What is the greatest common factor of 36 and 54?
A. 20
B. 19
C. 18
D. 17

28) Based on the table below, which of the following expressions represents any value of f in term of its corresponding value of x?
A. $f=x+1\frac{7}{8}$
B. $f=x-1\frac{7}{8}$
C. $f=2x+1\frac{7}{8}$
D. $f=2x-1\frac{7}{8}$

x	1.1	1.4	2.1
f	-0.775	-0.475	0.225

29) $10\ mm\ = ...?$
A. $0.001\ m$
B. $0.01\ m$
C. $100\ m$
D. $1000\ m$

30) A football team won exactly 60% of the games it played during last session. Which of the following could be the total number of games the team played last season?

A. 63
B. 55
C. 48
D. 37

31) 8 less than twice a positive integer is 70. What is the integer?
A. 80
B. 78
C. 40
D. 39

Types of air pollutions in 10 cities of a country

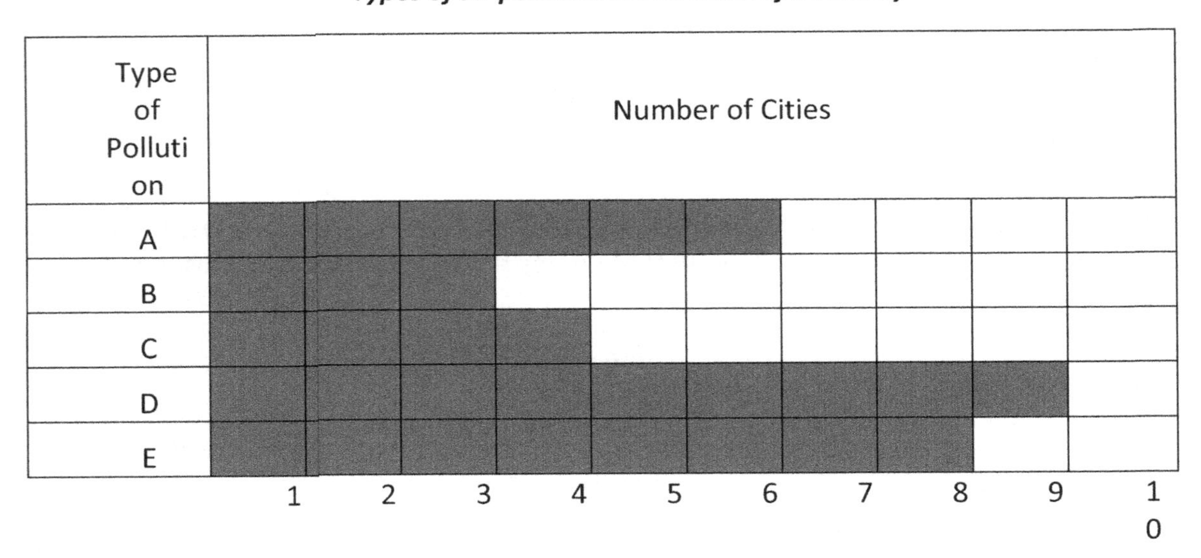

32) Based on the above data, what percent of cities are in the type of pollution A, C, and E respectively?

A. $60\%, 40\%, 90\%$
B. $30\%, 40\%, 90\%$
C. $30\%, 40\%, 60\%$
D. $40\%, 60\%, 90\%$

33) What is the missing term in the given sequence?

$$2, 7, 17, 37, 77, \_\_, 317$$

Write your answer in the box below.

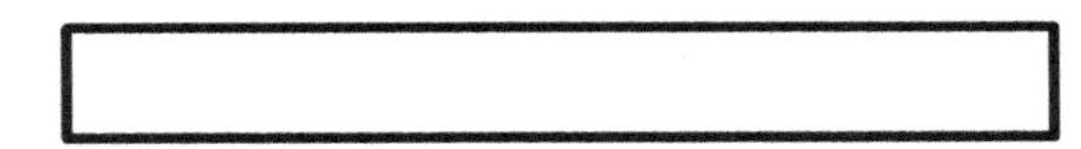

34) If $4x - 1 = 9$, what is the value of $2x + 10$?
A. 30.5
B. 25
C. 20.5
D. 15

35) How many tiles of $9\ cm^2$ is needed to cover a floor of dimension $7\ cm$ by $36\ cm$?

A. 26
B. 27
C. 28
D. 29

36) If there are 400 students at a school and nearly 37% of them prefer to learn Germany, approximately how many students want to learn Germany?

A. 400
B. 252
C. 148
D. 130

37) A shaft rotates 360 times in 12 seconds. How many times does it rotate in 18 seconds?

A. 540
B. 450
C. 360
D. 100

38) A card is drawn at random from a standard 52–card deck, what is the probability that the card is of the King? (There are 4 Kings in a standard 52-card deck.)

A. $\frac{1}{3}$
B. $\frac{1}{13}$
C. $\frac{1}{6}$
D. $\frac{1}{52}$

39) Which of the following statement can describe the following inequality correctly?

$$\frac{x}{5} \geq 9$$

A. David put x books in 5 shelves, and each shelf had at least 9 books.
B. David placed 5 books in x shelves so that each shelf had less than 9 books.
C. David put 9 books in x shelves and each shelf had exactly 5 books.
D. David put x books in 5 shelves, and each shelf had more than 9 books

40) Removing which of the following numbers will change the average of the numbers to 7.4?

$$1, 4, 5, 8, 11, 12$$

A. 4
B. 5
C. 8
D. 11

This is the end of Practice Test 1

STAAR Mathematics Practice Test 2

2020

Grade 6

Total number of questions: 40

Total time to complete the test: No time limit

You may use a calculator on this practice test.

STAAR Grade 6 Mathematics Reference Materials

AREA	
Triangle	$A = \frac{1}{2}bh$
Rectangle Parallelogram	$A = bh$
Trapezoid	$A = \frac{1}{2}h\,(b_1 + b_2)$
Circle	$A = \pi r^2$

VOLUME	
Rectangle Prism	$V = Bh$

LENGTH	
Customary	Metric
1 mile = 1,760 yards (yd)	1 kilometer (km) = 1,000 meter (m)
1 yard = 3 feet (ft)	1 meter (m) = 100 centimeters (cm)
1 foot (ft) = 12 inches (in.)	1 centimeter (cm) = 10 millimeters (mm)

VOLUME AND CAPACITY	
Customary	**Metric**
1 gallon (gal) = 4 quarts (qt)	1 liter (L) = 1,000 millimeters (mL)
1 quart (qt) = 2 pints (pt)	
1 pint (pt) = 2 cups (c)	
1 cup (c) = 8 fluid ounces (fl oz)	

WEIGHT AND MASS	
Customary	**Metric**
1 ton (T) = 2,000 Pounds (lb)	1 kilogram (kg) = 1,000 grams (g)
1 pound (lb) = 16 ounces (oz)	1 gram (g) = 1,000 milligrams (mg)

1) In the following figure, the shaded squares are what fractional part of the whole set of squares?

A. $\frac{1}{2}$

B. $\frac{5}{8}$

C. $\frac{2}{3}$

D. $\frac{3}{5}$

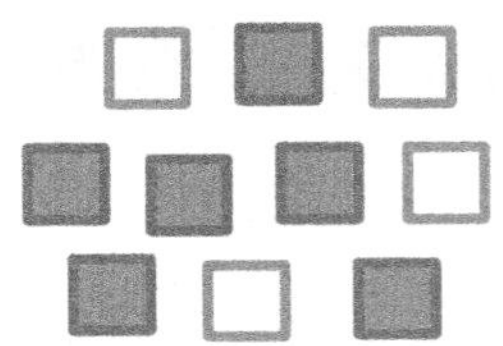

2) In a party, 14 soft drinks are required for every 16 guests. If there are 160 guests, how many soft drinks are required?

A. 18

B. 104

C. 140

D. 1,440

3) Which of the following statement is False?

A. $2 \times 2 = 4$

B. $(4 + 1) \times 5 = 25$

C. $6 \div (3 - 1) = 1$

D. $6 \times (4 - 2) = 12$

4) What is the value of 3^4 ?

Write your answer in the box below.

5) What is the volume of the following rectangle prism?

A. $19\ m^3$

B. $40\ m^3$

C. $50\ m^3$

D. $200\ m^3$

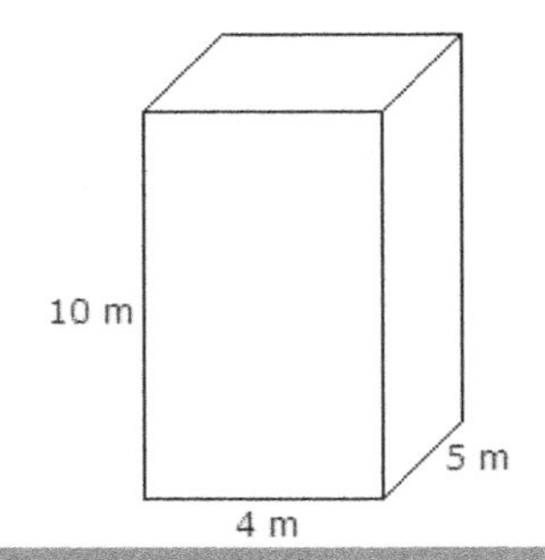

6) A shirt costing $\$500$ is discounted 25%. After a month, the shirt is discounted another 15%. Which of the following expressions can be used to find the selling price of the shirt?

A. $(500)(0.60)$

B. $(500) - 500(0.40)$

C. $(500)(0.25) - (200)(0.15)$

D. $(500)(0.75)(0.85)$

7) The area of a rectangle is x square feet and its length is 9 feet. Which equation represents y, the width of the rectangle in feet?

A. $y = \frac{x}{9}$

B. $y = \frac{9}{x}$

C. $y = 9x$

D. $y = 9 + x$

8) $(11 + 7) \div (3^3 \div 3) =$ __

A. 18

B. $\frac{5}{7}$

C. 2

D. 6

9) What is the missing prime factor of number 360?

$360 = 2^3 \times 3^2 \times$ __

Write your answer in the box below.

10) Which of the following shows the numbers from least to greatest? $\frac{11}{15}$, $75\%, 0.74, \frac{19}{25}$

A. $75\%, 0.74, \frac{11}{15}, \frac{19}{25}$

B. $75\%, 0.74, \frac{19}{25}, \frac{11}{15}$

C. $0.74, 75\%, \frac{11}{15}, \frac{19}{25}$

D. $\frac{11}{15}, 0.74, 75\%, \frac{19}{25}$

11) When 3 is added to four times a number M, the result is 24. Which of the following equations represents this statement?

A. $4 + 3M = 24$
B. $24M + 4 = 3$
C. $4M + 3 = 24$
D. $4M + 24 = 3$

12) The average of $13, 15, 20$ and x is 25. What is the value of x?

Write your answer in the box below.

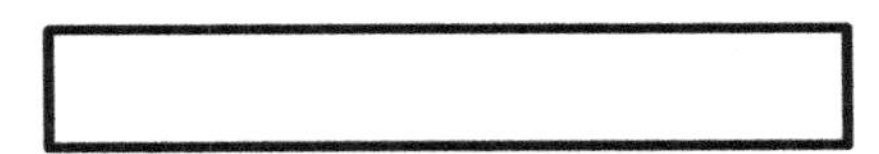

13) What is the Area of the square shown in the following square?

A. 2
B. 4
C. 6
D. 8

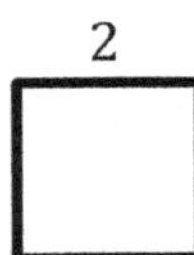

14) What is the value of this expression? $[3 \times (-14) - 48] - (-14) + [3 \times 8] \div 2$

Write your answer in the box below.

15) The price of a car was $28,000 in 2012. In 2013, the price of that car was $18,200. What was the rate of depreciation of the price of car per year?

A. 20%

B. 30%

C. 35%

D. 40%

16) How many possible outfit combinations come from five shirts, seven slacks, and five ties?

Write your answer in the box below.

17) An angle is equal to one fourth of its supplement. What is the measure of that angle?

A. 18

B. 24

C. 36

D. 45

18) John traveled 150 km in 6 hours and Alice traveled 180 km in 4 hours. What is the ratio of the average speed of John to average speed of Alice?

A. 3 : 2
B. 2 : 3
C. 5 : 9
D. 5 : 6

19) In five successive hours, a car travels 40 km, 45 km, 50 km, 35 km and 55 km. In the next five hours, it travels with an average speed of 50 km per hour. Find the total distance the car traveled in 10 hours.

A. $425\ km$
B. $450\ km$
C. $475\ km$
D. $500\ km$

20) How long does a 280–miles trip take moving at 50 miles per hour (mph)?

A. 5 hours
B. 5 hours and 24 minutes
C. 5 hours and 36 minutes
D. 5 hours and 48 minutes

21) The ratio of boys to girls in a school is $2:3$. If there are 600 students in a school, how many boys are in the school.

Write your answer in the box below.

22) 35 is What percent of 20?

A. 20%
B. 25%
C. 175%
D. 180%

23) The perimeter of the trapezoid below is 32. What is its area?

Write your answer in the box below.

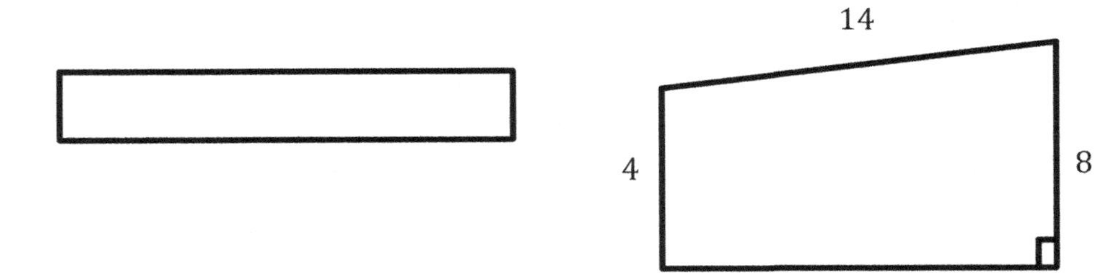

24) The area of a circle is less than 49π. Which of the following can be the circumference of the circle?

A. 8π
B. 14π
C. 16π
D. 32π

25) A $\$45$ shirt now selling for $\$28$ is discounted by about what percent?
A. 20%
B. 37.7%
C. 40%
D. 60%

26) In 1999, the average worker's income increased $\$3{,}000$ per year starting from $\$24{,}000$ annual salary. Which equation represents income greater than average?
(I = income, x = number of years after 1999)
A. $I > 3000\,x + 24000$
B. $I > -3000\,x + 24000$
C. $I < -3000\,x + 24000$
D. $I < 3000\,x - 24000$

27) From last year, the price of gasoline has increased from $\$1.40$ per gallon to $\$1.75$ per gallon. The new price is what percent of the original price?

A. 72%
B. 125%
C. 140%
D. 160%

28) Sophia purchased a sofa for $\$504$. The sofa is regularly priced at $\$600$. What was the percent discount Sophia received on the sofa?
A. 12%
B. 16%
C. 20%
D. 25%

29) A bag contains 20 balls: four green, five black, eight blue, a brown, a red and one white. If 19 balls are removed from the bag at random, what is the probability that a brown ball has been removed?

A. $\frac{1}{9}$
B. $\frac{1}{20}$
C. $\frac{4}{5}$
D. $\frac{19}{20}$

30) A rope weighs 600 grams per meter of length. What is the weight in kilograms of 15.2 meters of this rope? ($1\ kilograms\ = 1{,}000\ grams$)

A. 0.0912
B. 0.912
C. 9.12
D. 91.20

31) If $x = -8$, which equation is true?

A. $x(2x - 4) = 120$
B. $8\,(4 - x) = 96$
C. $2\,(4x + 6) = 79$
D. $6x - 2 = -46$

32) The price of a laptop is decreased by 10% to \$450. What is its original price?

A. 320
B. 380
C. 400
D. 500

33) What is the median of these numbers? 2, 27, 28, 19, 67, 44, 35

A. 19
B. 28
C. 44
D. 35

34) The radius of a cylinder is 6 inches and its height is 12 inches. What is the surface area of the cylinder in square inches?

Write your answer in the box below. (π equals 3.14) (Round your answer to the nearest whole number)

35) A bank is offering 4.5% simple interest on a savings account. If you deposit \$9,000, how much interest will you earn in five years?

A. \$405
B. \$720
C. \$2,025
D. \$3,600

36) Right triangle ABC has two legs of lengths $9\ cm\ (AB)$ and $12\ cm\ (AC)$. What is the length of the third side (BC)?

Write your answer in the box below.

37) Find the missing number in the sequence: $6, 9, 13, \ldots\ldots, 24$

A. 15
B. 17
C. 18
D. 20

38) 55 students took an exam and 11 of them failed. What percent of the students passed the exam?

Write your answer in the box below.

39) What is the sum of $\frac{8}{12}+\frac{4}{3}+\frac{2}{6}$?

A. 2.1
B. 3
C. $2\frac{1}{3}$
D. 1

40) What is 8,923.2769 rounded to the nearest tenth?

A. 8923.3
B. 8923.277
C. 8923
D. 8923.27

This is the end of Practice Test 2

STAAR Mathematics Practice Tests Answer Keys

Now, it's time to review your results to see where you went wrong and what areas you need to improve.

STAAR Math Practice Test 1				STAAR Math Practice Test 2			
1	B	**21**	5	**1**	D	**21**	240
2	C	**22**	C	**2**	C	**22**	C
3	D	**23**	C	**3**	C	**23**	36
4	C	**24**	A	**4**	81	**24**	A
5	B	**25**	D	**5**	D	**25**	B
6	D	**26**	C	**6**	D	**26**	A
7	D	**27**	C	**7**	A	**27**	B
8	D	**28**	B	**8**	C	**28**	B
9	D	**29**	B	**9**	5	**29**	D
10	B	**30**	B	**10**	D	**30**	C
11	A	**31**	D	**11**	C	**31**	B
12	C	**32**	A	**12**	52	**32**	D
13	C	**33**	157	**13**	B	**33**	B
14	D	**34**	D	**14**	-64	**34**	678
15	B	**35**	C	**15**	C	**35**	C
16	C	**36**	C	**16**	175	**36**	15
17	C	**37**	A	**17**	C	**37**	C
18	D	**38**	B	**18**	C	**38**	80
19	B	**39**	A	**19**	C	**39**	C
20	B	**40**	A	**20**	C	**40**	A

How to score your test

The basic score on each STAAR test is the raw score, which is simply the number of questions correct. On the STAAR test each subject test should be passed individually. It means that you must meet the standard on each section of the test. If you failed one subject test but did well enough on another, that's still not a passing score.

There are four possible scores that you can receive on the STAAR Math Grade 6 Test:

Do Not Meet: This indicates that your score is lower than the passing score. If you do not pass, you can reschedule to retake any the STAAR Math test. Students have three opportunities to retake test(s) and receive remedial help if they don't pass.

Approaches: This score indicates that your score meets the standard of t

Met the Standard: This indicates that your score meets Texas state standards for that subject.

Commended Performance: This indicates that you've mastered the skills that would be taught in your grade.

There are approximately 40 questions on STAAR Mathematics for grade 6. Similar to other subject areas, you will need a minimum score to pass the Mathematics Test. There are approximately 40 raw score points on the STAAR math test. The raw points correspond with correct answers. This will then be converted into your scaled score. Approximately, you need to get 28 out of 40 raw score to pass the STAAR Mathematics for grade 6.

To score your STAAR Mathematics practice tests, first find your raw score. There were 40 questions on each STAAR Mathematics practice test in this book. All questions have one point. Use the following table to convert your raw score to the scale score.

Raw Score	Scale Score	Result	Percentile
0	1065		0
1	1197	Do Not Meet	0
2	1276		0
3	1324		0
4	1359		0
5	1387		0
6	1411		0
7	1432		1
8	1451		2
9	1468		3
10	1484		4
11	1499		6
12	1513		8
13	1526		10
14	1539		12
15	1552		14
16	1564		16
17	1576		19
18	1588		22
19	1595	Approaches	25
20	1611		27
21	1622		30
22	1634		34
23	1645		37
24	1657		41
25	1669		44
26	1681		48
27	1693		52
28	1700	Meets	55
29	1719		60
30	1733		64
31	1747		68
32	1762		72
33	1779		76
34	1796		79
35	1815		83
36	1836		87
37	1854	Masters	89
38	1889		93
39	1925		96
40 or more	1973-2185		98-100

STAAR Mathematics Practice Tests Answers and Explanations

STAAR Mathematics Practice Test 1

Answers and Explanations

1) Choice B is correct

$4(1.052) - 3.126 = 4.208 - 3.126 = 1.082$

2) Choice C is correct

$-12 < -4 < -2 < -1 < 1 < 3 < 7$

Then choice C is correct

3) Choice D is correct

First, we need to find the GCF (Greatest Common Factor) of 143 and 55. $143 = 11 \times 13$

$55 = 5 \times 11$ → GFC = 11. Therefore, we need 11 boxes.

4) Choice C is correct

$$2{,}205 \div 315 = \frac{2{,}205}{315} = \frac{441}{63} = \frac{147}{21} = 7$$

5) Choice B is correct

$112 = 22 + x$. Subtract 22 from both sides of the equation. Then: $x = 112 - 22 = 90$

6) Choice D is correct

Distance that car B travels $=$ $1.2 \times$ distance that car A travels

$= 1.2 \times 221.5 = 265.8$ Km

7) Choice D is correct

The perimeter of the trapezoid is 38.

Therefore, the missing side (height) is = 38 – 8 – 10 – 11 = 9

Area of the trapezoid: $A = \frac{1}{2} h (b1 + b2) = \frac{1}{2} (9) (8 + 10) = 81$

8) Choice D is correct

A. $3^1 + 12 = 3 + 12 = 15$

B. $3^3 - 3^2 = 27 - 9 = 18$

C. $3^4 - 60 = 81 - 60 = 21$

D. $3^5 - 218 = 243 - 218 = 25$

9) Choice D is correct

The radius of the circle is: $\frac{\pi}{2}$. The area of circle: $\pi r^2 = \pi(\frac{\pi}{2})^2 = \pi \times \frac{\pi^2}{4} = \frac{\pi^3}{4}$

10) Choice B is correct

Alfred has x apple which is 15 apples more than number of apples Alvin owns. Therefore:

$x - 15 = 40 \rightarrow x = 40 + 15 = 55$. Alfred has 55 apples. Let y be the number of apples that Baron has. Then: $y = \frac{1}{5} \times 55 = 11$

11) Choice A is correct

Complementary angles add up to 180 degrees. $\beta + 150° = 180° \rightarrow \beta = 180° - 150° = 30°$

The sum of all angles in a triangle is 180 degrees. Then: $\alpha + \beta + 50° = 180° \rightarrow$

$\alpha + 30° + 50° = 180° \rightarrow \alpha + 80° = 180° \rightarrow \alpha = 180° - 80° = 100°$

12) Choice C is correct

Let x be the original price. If the price of a laptop is decreased by 15% to $425, then:
$85\ \%\ of\ x = 425 \Rightarrow 0.85x = 425 \Rightarrow x = 425 \div 0.85 = 500$

13) Choice C is correct

Let x and y be two sides of the shape. Then:

$x + 1 = 1 + 1 + 1 \rightarrow x = 2$

$y + 6 + 2 = 5 + 4 \rightarrow y + 8 = 9 \rightarrow y = 1$

Then, the perimeter is:

$1 + 5 + 1 + 4 + 1 + 2 + 1 + 6 + 2 + 1 = 24$

14) Choice D is correct

Two months, April and August, in 12 months start with A, then:

Probability = $\frac{number\ of\ desired\ outcomes}{\text{number of total outcomes}} = \frac{2}{12} = \frac{1}{6}$

15) Choice B is correct

First, put the numbers in order from least to greatest: 1, 1, 1, 2, 3, 3, 3, 4, 5, 6, 6

The Mode of the set of numbers is: 1 and 3 (the most frequent numbers)

Median is: 3 (the number in the middle)

16) Choice C is correct

$x \times 92 = x \times (90 + 2) = (x \times 90) + (x \times 2)$

17) Choice C is correct

The ratio of pens to pencils is 3 : 5. Therefore there are 3 pens out of all 8 pens and pencils. To find the answer, first divide 96 by 8 then multiply the result by 3. $96 \div 8 = 12 \rightarrow 12 \times 3 = 36$

There are 36 pens and 60 pencils (96-36). Therefore, 24 more pens should be put in the box to make the ratio 1 : 1

18) Choice D is correct

If the value of point A is greater than the value of point B, then the distance of two points on the number line is: value of A— value of B

A. $-\frac{24}{3} - (-13) = -8 + 13 = 5 = 5$

B. $-3 - \left(-\frac{24}{3}\right) = -3 + 8 = 5 = 5$

C. $-2 - \left(-\frac{24}{3}\right) = -2 + 8 = 6 \neq 5$

Both A and B are 5 points from $-\frac{24}{3}$. Choice D is correct.

19) Choice B is correct

$\frac{3}{13} \cong 0.23$ $\frac{5}{14} \cong 0.357$ $\frac{4}{11} \cong 0.36$ $\frac{2}{5} = 0.4$

Then:

$$\frac{3}{13} < \frac{5}{14} < \frac{4}{11} < \frac{2}{5}$$

20) Choice B is correct

Plug in the value of x in the equations. $x = -4$, then:

E. $x(3x-1) = 50 \rightarrow -4(3(-4)-1) = -4(-12-1) = -4(-13) = 52 \neq 50$

F. $5(11-x^2) = -25 \rightarrow 5(11-(-4)^2) = 5(11-16) = 5(-5) = -25$

G. $3(-2x+5) = 49 \rightarrow 3(-2(-4)+5) = 3(8+5) = 39 \neq 49$

H. $x(-5x-19) = -3 \rightarrow -4(-5(-4)-19 = -4(20-19) = -4 \neq -3$

21) The answer is 5.

Let x be the missing prime factor of 450. $450 = 2 \times 3 \times 3 \times x \Rightarrow x = \frac{450}{18} \Rightarrow x = 25 = 5 \times 5$

$450 = 2^1 \times 3^2 \times 5^2$ The missing prime factor of 450 is 5.

22) Choice C is correct

Use Pythagorean theorem to find the hypotenuse of the triangle.

$$a^2 + b^2 = c^2 \rightarrow 6^2 + 8^2 = c^2 \rightarrow 36 + 64 = c^2 \rightarrow 100 = c^2 \rightarrow c = 10$$

The perimeter of the triangle is: $6 + 8 + 10 = 24$

23) Choice C is correct

$\frac{65}{50} = 1.30 = 130\%$. The answer is 130%.

24) Choice A is correct

Let's check the options provided.

E. $-10 + (-8) + \frac{-5}{2} \times 2 \rightarrow -10 + (-8) + \frac{-5}{2} \times 2 = -10 + (-8) + (-5) = -10 - 13 = -23$

F. $5 \times 3 + (-2) \times 18 = 15 + (-38) = -21$

G. $-10 + 6 \times 8 \div (-4) = -10 + 48 \div (-4) = -10 - 12 = -22$

H. $(-3) \times (-7) + 2 = 21 + 2 = 23$

25) Choice D is correct

$1\ feet = 12\ inches$. Then: $300\ in. \times \frac{1\ ft}{12\ in} = \frac{300}{12}\ ft = 25\ ft$

26) Choice C is correct

A. $0.09 = \frac{9}{100}$

B. $\frac{20}{100} = \frac{2}{10} = 0.2$

C. $2.4 = 2\frac{4}{10} = \frac{24}{10}$

D. $\frac{35}{7} = 5$

Only choice C is correct.

27) Choice C is correct

Prime factorizing of $36 = 2 \times 2 \times 3 \times 3$

Prime factorizing of $54 = 2 \times 3 \times 3 \times 3$

To find Greatest Common Factor, multiply the common factors of both numbers.

GCF$= 2 \times 3 \times 3 = 18$

28) Choice B is correct

Plug in the values of x in the equations provided.

A. $f = x + 1\frac{7}{8} = 1.1 + 1\frac{7}{8} = 1.1 + \frac{15}{8} = 2.975 \neq -0.775$

B. $f = x - 1\frac{7}{8} = 1.1 - 1\frac{7}{8} = -0.775$

C. $f = 2x + 1\frac{7}{8} = 2(1.1) + \frac{15}{8} = 4.075 \neq -0.775$

D. $f = 2x - 1\frac{7}{8} = 2(1.1) - \frac{15}{8} = 0.325 \neq -0.775$

29) Choice B is correct

$1\ m = 1000\ mm$ and $1\ mm = 0.001\ m$

Then, $10\ mm = 10 \times 0.001\ m = 0.01\ m$

30) Choice B is correct

Choices A, C and D are incorrect because 60% of each of the numbers is a non-whole number.

E. 63, $60\%\ of\ 63 = 0.60 \times 63 = 37.8$

F. 55, $60\%\ of\ 55 = 0.60 \times 55 = 33$

G. 48, $60\%\ of\ 48 = 0.60 \times 48 = 28.8$

H. 37, $60\%\ of\ 37 = 0.60 \times 37 = 22.2$

31) Choice D is correct

Let x be the integer. Then: $2x - 8 = 70$. Add 8 both sides: $2x = 78$. Divide both sides by 2:

$x = 39$

32) Choice A is correct

Percent of cities in the type of pollution A: $\frac{6}{10} \times 100 = 60\%$

Percent of cities in the type of pollution C: $\frac{4}{10} \times 100 = 40\%$

Percent of cities in the type of pollution E: $\frac{9}{10} \times 100 = 90\%$

33) The answer is 157

Find the difference of each pairs of numbers: 2, 7, 17, 37, 77, ____, 317

The difference of 2 and 7 is 5, 7 and 17 is 10, 17 and 37 is 20, 37 and 77 is 40, 77 and next number should be 80. The number is 77 + 80 = 157

34) Choice D is correct

$4x - 1 = 9 \rightarrow 4x = 9 + 1 = 10 \rightarrow x = \frac{10}{4} = 2.5$

Then, $2x + 10 = 2(2.5) + 10 = 5 + 10 = 15$

35) Choice C is correct

The area of the floor is: 7 cm × 36 cm = 252 cm

The number of tiles needed = 252 ÷ 9 = 28

36) Choice C is correct

Number of students prefer to learn Germany= $37\% of 400 = \frac{37}{100} \times 400 = 148$

37) Choice A is correct

The shaft rotates 360 times in 12 seconds. Then, the number of rotates in 18 second equals to:

$$\frac{360 \times 18}{12} = 540$$

38) Choice B is correct

The probability of choosing a King is $\frac{4}{52} = \frac{1}{13}$

39) Choice A is correct

Let's write an inequality for each statement.

A. $\frac{x}{5} \geq 9$ (this is the same as the inequality provided)

B. $\frac{5}{x} < 9$

C. $\frac{9}{x} = 5$

D. $\frac{x}{5} > 9$

40) Choice A is correct

Check each choice provided:

A. 4 $\frac{1+5+8+11+12}{5} = \frac{37}{5} = 7.4$

B. 5 $\frac{1+4+8+11+12}{5} = \frac{36}{5} = 7.2$

C. 8 $\frac{1+4+5+11+12}{5} = \frac{36}{5} = 6.6$

D. 11 $\frac{1+4+5+8+12}{5} = \frac{30}{5} = 6$

STAAR Mathematics Practice Test 2

Answers and Explanations

1) Choice D is correct.

There are 10 squares and 6 of them are shaded. Therefore, 6 out of 10 or $\frac{6}{10} = \frac{3}{5}$ are shaded.

2) Choice C is correct

Let x be the number of soft drinks for 252 guests. It's needed to have a proportional ratio to find x. $\frac{14 \text{ soft drinks}}{16 \text{ guests}} = \frac{x}{160 \text{ guests}} \Rightarrow x = \frac{160 \times 14}{16} \Rightarrow x = 140$

3) Choice C is correct.

Let's review the choices provided:

A. $2 \times 2 = 4$ This is true!

B. $(4+1) \times 5 = 25$ This is true!

C. $6 \div (3-1) = 1 \rightarrow 6 \div 2 = 3$ This is NOT true!

D. $6 \times (4-2) = 12 \rightarrow 6 \times 2 = 12$ This is true!

4) The answer is 81

$3^4 = 3 \times 3 \times 3 \times 3 = 81$

5) Choice D is correct.

$V = lwh \rightarrow V = 4 \times 5 \times 10 = 200$

6) Choice D is correct

To find the discount, multiply the number by $(100\% - rate\ of\ discount)$.

Therefore, for the first discount we get: $(500)(100\% - 25\%) = (500)(0.75)$

For the next 15% discount: $(500)(0.75)(0.85)$

7) Choice A is correct

$Area = L \times W \rightarrow x = 9 \times W \rightarrow W = y$

then: $x = 9 \times W \rightarrow x = 9 \times y \rightarrow y = \frac{x}{9}$

8) Choice C is correct

$(11 + 7) \div (3^3 \div 3) = (18) \div (27 \div 3) = (18) \div (9) = 2$

9) The answer is 5

$360 = 2^3 \times 3^2 \times 5^1$

10) Choice D is correct

Change the numbers to decimal and then compare. $\frac{11}{15} = 0.73 \ldots, 0.74, 75\% = 0.75, \frac{19}{25} = 0.76$

Therefore: $\frac{11}{15} < 0.74 < 75\% < \frac{19}{25}$

11) Choice C is correct.

$3 + (4 \times M) = 24 \rightarrow 4M + 3 = 24$

12) The answer is 52.

$$\text{average} = \frac{\text{sum of terms}}{\text{number of terms}} \Rightarrow 25 = \frac{13 + 15 + 20 + x}{4} \Rightarrow 100 = 48 + x \Rightarrow x = 52$$

13) Choice B is correct.

$Area\ of\ a\ square = (one\ side) \times (one\ side) = 2 \times 2 = 4$

14) The answer is: -64

Use PEMDAS (order of operation): $[3 \times (-14) - 48] — 14 + [3 \times 8] \div 2 =$

$$[-42 - 48] + 14 + 24 \div 2 = -90 + 14 + 12 = -64$$

15) Choice C is correct

Use this formula: Percent of Change: $\frac{\text{New Value} - \text{Old Value}}{Old\ Value} \times 100\%$

$\frac{28{,}000 - 18{,}200}{28{,}000} \times 100\% = -35\%$. The negative sign means that the price decreased.

16) The answer is 175.

To find the number of possible outfit combinations, multiply number of options for each factor: $5 \times 7 \times 5 = 175$

17) Choice C is correct

The sum of supplement angles is 180. Let x be that angle. Therefore, $x + 4x = 180$

$5x = 180$, divide both sides by 5: $x = 36$

18) Choice C is correct

The average speed of John is: $150 \div 6 = 25\ km$

The average speed of Alice is: $180 \div 4 = 45\ km$

Write the ratio and simplify: $25: 45 \Rightarrow 5: 9$

19) Choice C is correct

Add the first 5 numbers. $40 + 45 + 50 + 35 + 55 = 225$

To find the distance traveled in the next 5 hours, multiply the average by number of hours.

$Distance = Average \times Rate = 50 \times 5 = 250$

Add both numbers: $250 + 225 = 475$

20) Choice C is correct

Use distance formula: $Distance = Rate \times time \Rightarrow 280 = 50 \times T$, divide both sides by 50.

$\frac{280}{50} = T \Rightarrow T = 5.6$ hours. Change hours to minutes for the decimal part. $0.6\ hours = 0.6 \times 60 = 36\ minutes$.

21) The answer is 240.

The ratio of boy to girls is $2:3$. Therefore, there are 2 boys out of 5 students. To find the answer, first divide the total number of students by 5, then multiply the result by 2.

$600 \div 5 = 120 \Rightarrow 120 \times 2 = 240$

22) Choice C is correct

$\frac{35}{20} = 1.75 = 175\%$

23) The answer is 36.

The perimeter of the trapezoid is $32\ cm$. Therefore, the missing side (height) is

$32 - 14 - 8 - 4 = 6$. Area of a trapezoid: $A = \frac{1}{2} h\,(b_1 + b_2) = \frac{1}{2}\,(6)(8 + 4) = 36$

24) Choice A is correct

Area of the circle is less than $14\,\pi$. Use the formula of areas of circles.

$Area = \pi r^2 \Rightarrow 49\,\pi > \pi r^2 \Rightarrow 49 > r^2 \Rightarrow r < 7$

Radius of the circle is less than 7. Let's put 7 for the radius. Now, use the circumference formula: $Circumference = 2\pi r = 2\pi\,(7) = 14\pi$. Since the radius of the circle is less than 7. Then, the circumference of the circle must be less than 14π. Only choice A is less than 14π.

25) Choice B is correct

Use the formula for Percent of Change: $\frac{\text{New Value} - \text{Old Value}}{Old\ Value} \times 100\%$.

$\frac{28-45}{45} \times 100\% = -37.7\%$ (negative sign here means that the new price is less than old price).

26) Choice A is correct

Let x be the number of years. Therefore, \$3,000 per year equals $3000x$.

starting from \$24,000 annual salary means you should add that amount to $3000x$.

Income more than that is: $I > 3{,}000x + 24{,}000$

27) Choice B is correct

The question is this: 1.75 is what percent of 1.40?

$$\frac{1.75}{1.40} = 1.25 = 125\%$$

28) Choice B is correct

$\frac{504}{600} = 0.84 = 84\%$. 504 is 84% of 600. Therefore, the discount is: $100\% - 84\% = 16\%$

29) Choice D is correct

If 19 balls are removed from the bag at random, there will be one ball in the bag. The probability of choosing a brown ball is 1 out of 20. Therefore, the probability of not choosing a brown ball is 19 out of 20 and the probability of having not a brown ball after removing 19 balls is the same.

30) Choice C is correct

The weight of 15.2 meters of this rope is: $15.2 \times 600\ g = 9{,}120\ g$, $1\ kg = 1{,}000\ g$, therefore, $7{,}320\ g \div 1000 = 9.12\ kg$

31) Choice B is correct.

Only choice B is correct. Other choices don't work in the equation. $8\ (4 - (-8)) = 96$

32) Choice D is correct

Let x be the original price. If the price of a laptop is decreased by 10% to \$450, then:

$90\%\ of\ x = 450 \Rightarrow 0.90x = 450 \Rightarrow x = 450 \div 0.90 = 500$

33) Choice B is correct

Write the numbers in order: $2, 19, 27, 28, 35, 44, 67$.

Median is the number in the middle. So, the median is 28.

34) The answer is 678.

Surface Area of a cylinder $= 2\pi r(r + h)$, The radius of the cylinder is 6 inches and its height is 12 inches. π is about 3.14. Then: Surface Area of a cylinder $= 2(\pi)(6)(6 + 12) = 216\ \pi = 678.24 \approx 678$

35) Choice C is correct

Use simple interest formula: $I = prt$ ($I = interest, p = principal, r = rate, t = time$)

$I = (9{,}000)(0.045)(5) = 2{,}025$

36) The answer is 15.

Use Pythagorean Theorem: $a^2 + b^2 = c^2$

$9^2 + 12^2 = c^2 \Rightarrow 81 + 144 = c^2 \Rightarrow 225 = c^2 \Rightarrow c = 15$

37) Choice C is correct.

$6 + 3 = 9$, $9 + 4 = 13$, $13 + 5 = 18$, $18 + 6 = 24$

38) The answer is 80.

The failing rate is 11 out of $55 = \frac{11}{55}$

Change the fraction to percent: $\frac{11}{55} \times 100\% = 20\%$

20 percent of students failed. Therefore, 80 percent of students passed the exam.

39) Choice C is correct

$$\frac{8}{12} + \frac{4}{3} + \frac{2}{6} = \frac{8 + 4(4) + 2(2)}{12} = \frac{28}{12} = \frac{7}{3} = 2\frac{1}{3}$$

40) Choice A is correct

The tenth value is 2.

8923.27 is closer to 8923.3 than 8923.2

"Effortless Math Education" Publications

Effortless Math authors' team strives to prepare and publish the best quality STAAR Mathematics learning resources to make learning Math easier for all. We hope that our publications help you learn Math in an effective way and prepare for the STAAR test.

We all in Effortless Math wish you good luck and successful studies!

Effortless Math Authors

www.EffortlessMath.com

... So Much More Online!

- ✓ FREE Math lessons
- ✓ More Math learning books!
- ✓ Mathematics Worksheets
- ✓ Online Math Tutors

Need a PDF version of this book?

Visit www.EffortlessMath.com

Made in the USA
Middletown, DE
05 May 2021

39014026R00084